UNIVERSITY OF MAINE
LIBRARIES

Raymond H. Fogler Library
ORONO

Amino Acids and
Serum Proteins

Amino Acids and Serum Proteins

Based on the Richard J. Block Memorial Symposium sponsored by the Division of Biological Chemistry at the 142nd Meeting of the American Chemical Society, Atlantic City, N. J., September 11, 1962

Jacob A. Stekol, *Symposium Chairman*

ADVANCES IN CHEMISTRY SERIES **44**

AMERICAN CHEMICAL SOCIETY
WASHINGTON, D.C. 1964

Copyright © 1964

American Chemical Society

All Rights Reserved

Library of Congress Catalog Card 64–16321

PRINTED IN THE UNITED STATES OF AMERICA

Advances in Chemistry Series
Robert F. Gould, *Editor*

Advisory Board

Fred Basolo

Raymond F. Boyer

John H. Fletcher

Jack Halpern

Wayne W. Hilty

George W. Irving

Amel R. Menotti

Walter C. Saeman

Leo H. Sommer

AMERICAN CHEMICAL SOCIETY
APPLIED PUBLICATIONS

Contributors

Richard J. Block, Boyce Thompson Institute for Plant Research, Yonkers, N. Y.

Amubha Chowdhury, Department of Radiation Biology, University of Rochester School of Medicine and Dentistry, Rochester, N. Y.

Thomas W. Cook, Boyce Thompson Institute for Plant Research, Yonkers, N. Y.

Vincent du Vigneaud, Department of Biochemistry, Cornell University Medical College, New York, N. Y.

Santiago Grisolia, Department of Biochemistry, School of Medicine, University of Kansas Medical Center, Kansas City, Kansas.

Merton L. Groves, Eastern Regional Research Laboratory, Philadelphia, Pa.

Helen R. Hanavan, Department of Radiation Biology, University of Rochester School of Medicine and Dentistry, Rochester, N. Y.

S. Mark Henry, Boyce Thompson Institute for Plant Research, Yonkers, N. Y.

Norbert J. Hipp, Eastern Regional Research Laboratory, Philadelphia, Pa.

Joseph T. Holden, Department of Biochemistry, City of Hope Medical Center, Duarte, Calif.

James M. Manning, Department of Biochemistry, Tufts University School of Medicine, Boston, Mass.

Thomas L. McMeekin, Eastern Regional Research Laboratory, Philadelphia, Pa.

Alton Meister, Department of Biochemistry, Tufts University School of Medicine, Boston, Mass.

Leon L. Miller, Department of Radiation Biology, University of Rochester School of Medicine and Dentistry, Rochester, N. Y.

Kivie Moldave, Department of Biochemistry, Tufts University School of Medicine, Boston, Mass.

Fred Plum, Department of Biochemistry, Cornell University Medical College, New York, N. Y.

Julian R. Rachele, Department of Biochemistry, Cornell University Medical College, New York, N. Y.

Luisa Raijman, Department of Biochemistry, School of Medicine, University of Kansas, Kansas City, Kansas.

Lester J. Reed, Department of Biochemistry, Cornell University Medical College, New York, N. Y.

Julius Schultz, Department of Biochemistry, Hahnemann Medical College, Philadelphia, Pa.

Jakob A. Stekol, Department of Physiological Chemistry and Nutrition, Institute for Cancer Research, Philadelphia, Pa.

Neville Stone, Department of Biochemistry, Tufts University School of Medicine, Boston, Mass.

Nantha Titthasiri, Department of Radiation Biology, University of Rochester School of Medicine and Dentistry, Rochester, N. Y.

Gerrit Toennies, Department of General Biochemistry, Institute for Cancer Research, Philadelphia, Pa.

John E. Wilson, Department of Biochemistry, Cornell University Medical College, New York, N. Y.

Preface

The tragic death of Dr. Richard J. Block in February 1962 was a great shock to his friends and colleagues. The members of the Executive Committee of the Division of Biological Chemistry who were familiar with his work proposed at the March 1962 meeting in Washington that a symposium be held in recognition of his lifetime efforts in advancing knowledge in amino acid and protein biochemistry. It is particularly important that in spite of Richard Block's reluctance to participate in Society affairs, other than to offer papers for presentation and to accept invitations to take part in symposia, the Executive Committee was willing on the basis of his reputation to sponsor a symposium in his honor at the national meeting of the American Chemical Society held in Atlantic City in September 1962. It is from this symposium that papers of this volume originated, in addition to investigations of other authors, who would have wished to participate but were pressed with other commitments.

The Executive Committee was especially fortunate in the ready acceptance by such an eminent biochemist as Dr. Jack Stekol to take on the duties of both the organization of the Richard J. Block Memorial Symposium and the creation of this volume. Such labors and those of the participants are a reflection of the deep regard in which Dr. Block was held by his colleagues.

It was fitting that Dr. Stekol, a lifetime friend, introduce this volume with a review of Richard Block's life and his scientific work. In the extensive bibliography included in this account, one finds a number of books and reviews, some of which serve today as "bibles" for laboratory procedures both for amino acid and protein research; and how many of us in the past consulted "Block and Bolling" for the amino acid composition of proteins! As students over a quarter of a century ago, some of us wondered why the title of some of Block's papers bore no relation to the contents. This was his way of overcoming "administrative" pressures as to what should be done in the laboratory, a problem that is particularly topical today when Congressional committees are questioning the freedom to "change" the direction of one's research. Block was a pioneer in this respect; the title satisfied the administrators who were not sufficiently knowledgeable to recognize that the research bore no obvious relation to the title. Yet today at the National Institute of Mental Health and Neurological Institutes around the country, basic research on amino acids and proteins, not too much unlike Block's, is prevalent. In this respect the papers included in this volume, though apparently diverse, yet reflect a certain interrelationship well within the scope of Block's general interest and serve as an adequate tribute to his contributions.

JULIUS SCHULTZ,
Secretary

Division of Biological Chemistry,
American Chemical Society

CONTENTS

Preface vii

Richard Joseph Block, 1906-1962—A Biography xiii

Bibliography of the Published Work of Richard J. Block xiv

1. The Nature and Origin of the Serum Proteins 1
   Julius Schultz, Institute for Biochemical Studies in Cancer, Department of Biochemistry, Hahnemann Medical College, Philadelphia, Pa.

2. Dominant Role of the Liver in Biosynthesis of the Plasma Proteins with Special Reference to the Plasma Mucoproteins (Seromucoid), Ceruloplasmin, and Fibrinogen 17
   Leon L. Miller, Helen R. Hanavan, Nantha Titthasiri, and *Anubha Chowdhury*, Department of Radiation Biology, School of Medicine and Dentistry, University of Rochester, Rochester, N. Y.

3. Protein Biosynthesis—Aminoacyl Transfer from sRNA to Ribosomes 41
   Kivie Moldave, Department of Biochemistry, Tufts University, School of Medicine, Boston, Mass.

4. Refractive Indices of Amino Acids, Proteins, and Related Substances 54
   Thomas L. McMeekin, Merton L. Groves, and *Norbert J. Hipp*, Eastern Regional Research Laboratory, Philadelphia, Pa.

5. Conversion of Proline to Hydroxyproline in Collagen Synthesis 67
   Alton Meister, Neville Stone, and *James M. Manning*, Department of Biochemistry, Tufts University Shool of Medicine, Boston, Mass.

6. **The Administration of Radioactive L—Cystathionine to a Human Cystinuric** 82
   Vincent du Vigneaud, Julian R. Rachele, John E. Wilson, Fred Plum, and *Lester J. Reed,* Department of Biochemistry, and Department of Medicine, Cornell University Medical College, and New York Hospital, New York, N.Y.

7. **Methionine Sulfoxide and Other Combined Amino Acids in the German Cockroach** 85
   S. Mark Henry, Richard J. Block, and *Thomas W. Cook,* Boyce Thompson Institute for Plant Research, Inc., Yonkers, N.Y.

8. **Amino Acid Transport in Bacteria—Effect of Nutritional and Physiological Factors** 96
   Joseph T. Holden, Department of Biochemistry, Medical Research Institute, City of Hope Medical Center, Duarte, Calif.

9. **Differential Responses to Amino Acids in Bacterial Growth** — 118
   Gerrit Toennies, The Institute for Cancer Research, Philadelphia, Pa.

10. **Biosynthesis and Utilization of Acetyl Phosphate, Formyl Phosphate, and Carbamyl Phosphate and their Relations to the Urea Cycle** 128
    Santiago Grisolia and *Luisa Raijman,* Department of Biochemistry, University of Kansas, Kansas City, Kans.

Index 150

Richard Joseph Block

Richard Joseph Block
1906 - 1962

Richard Block and his wife, together with Dr. and Mrs. Jerome A. Uram and 14 other persons, died in a plane crash on February 4, 1962, shortly after leaving Tingo Maria, Peru. The Americans were on a mission sponsored by the National Institutes of Health in connection with the International Program on Nutrition Studies. His untimely death shocked his friends and colleagues, and brought to an abrupt end his active and productive career. The bibliography of his published work, printed on pages xvi through xxiii, will give some idea of the scope of his activities in the past 30 years, during which he collaborated with over 70 scientists. Block left numerous projects "on the fire." Most important of all, he left behind him friends who deeply feel the loss of such a rare human being. This was his greatest achievement.

He was born in Macon, Ga., on May 4, 1906, and received his B.S. in chemistry in 1928 and his Ph.D. in physiological chemistry in 1931 at Yale. While at Yale he received research inspiration, which never left him throughout life, from Professor L. B. Mendel, to whose memory Block remained fiercely loyal. Block was a friend to his friends. While he acknowledged his enemies, he ignored them, not permitting them to affect his way of life or his convictions. To him enemies were like booby traps or dangerous leaks in the roof: They merely required attention of a strictly technical nature.

His heart and mind were in his beloved amino acids and proteins, and among the amino acids those containing sulfur received a great deal of attention from him and his collaborators. In collaboration with R. Jackson, Block was among the first to establish the nutritional role of methionine and to point to the probable pathway of the conversion of its sulfur to that of cysteine. That was accomplished at a time when tracer methodology was only a gleam in the eye of the biochemist, and one's ingenuity and imagination had to be strained to the utmost in order to design and execute experiments which would be next best to a direct demonstration of the convertibility of one metabolite into another.

He studied the synthesis and utilization of sulfur-containing compounds in man, rat, dog, goat, cow, ewe, bacteria, yeasts, cockroach, and algae, constantly being aware that the results are good only as the methods which were employed to obtain them. He devoted a great deal of his time to the development of better and more refined chemical and chromatographic methods for the isolation and determination of amino acids in proteins from a variety of sources, and he had even set up a laboratory in his house for the purpose, where he worked at all hours.

Much time and effort were spent in compiling the analytical and preparative procedures for studying the amino acid composition of proteins of animal and plant origin, which resulted in his first book, "The Determination of the Amino Acids," followed by five more dealing with the amino acid composition of proteins and foods, paper chromatographic and electrophoretic methods, and analytical methods of protein chemistry.

This activity had its practical objective—namely, to establish, in accord with the views of L. B. Mendel and his students, the correlation of the amino acid composition of proteins with their nutritional value. In collaboration with H. H. Mitchell this objective was accomplished.

In 1933 Block proposed the "anlage" hypothesis, which postulates that certain structures of relatively constant composition are common to all the serum proteins. In the last 5 years of his life Block devoted his efforts to further development of this anlage hypothesis, applying more rigorous and newer methods which have become available. Truly, as Max Planck has remarked, scientists never give up their theories, and they appear to give them up only because they die. It would appear that this theory in one form or another, undoubtedly with modifications, deletions, additions, etc., beyond recognition of the original, will be developed further and even, perhaps, linked to the genetic code governing the protein structure and its biological properties.

While engaged in these activities, Block found time and energy to serve as professorial lecturer at New York Medical College; a visiting professor in the Department of Physiology and Biochemistry and an associate member of the Bureau of Biological Research of Rutgers University; chairman of the Sub-Committee on Biological Chemistry of the National Research Council; and a member of the Nutrition Study Section of the National Institutes of Health. He was a member of the American Chemical Society, American Society of Biological Chemists, American Institute of Nutrition, Society for Experimental Biology and Medicine, New York Academy of Sciences, American Institute of Chemists, AAAS, and Sigma Xi.

Block is survived by two daughters, Mrs. Werner Krebser and Mrs. Thomas Montie. Ralph Holman of the University of Minnesota, who was in Lima on a mission similar to that of Block, writes:

> I delayed my departure from Lima in order that I could attend the funeral, for I had ascertained from the American Consul the interment was to be in Lima and none of the families would be present. The ceremony was simple and beautiful. Ambassador James Loeb spoke on behalf of the Government and recounted the accomplishments of the deceased and their mission to Latin America. Dr. Orlando Olsesse, President of the Universidad Agraria in Peru, next spoke on behalf of the Peruvians, expressing the gratitude they hold for Drs. Block and Uram in coming to aid in the relief of the nutritional problems of the country. He expressed the grief of the Peruvian scientists in the untimely death of such friends.

A symposium to honor the memory of R. J. Block was organized with the aid of the Division of Biological Chemistry of the American Chemical Society and held in September 1962 in Atlantic City, N. J. The papers presented at this symposium, together with additional contributions from several recognized authorities in their respective fields, are presented in this memorial volume as a tribute to R. J. Block from his friends and colleagues and as a wreath on his lonely grave in a foreign land.

J. A. STEKOL

The Institute for Cancer Research
Philadelphia, Pa.

Bibliography of the Published Work of Richard J. Block

Scientific Papers and Chapters of Books

(1) The basic amino acids of wool. J. Biol. Chem., 86, 107 (1930). With H. B. Vickery.
(2) The basic amino acids of silk fibroin. Determination of the basic amino acids yielded by proteins. Ibid., 93, 105 (1931). With H. B. Vickery.
(3) The basic amino acids of proteins. A chemical relationship between various keratins. Ibid., 93, 113 (1931). With H. B. Vickery.
(4) Metabolism of cystine and methionine. Science, 74, 414 (1931). With R. W. Jackson.
(5) The basic amino acids from neurokeratin: Is neurokeratin a true keratin? J. Biol. Chem., 94, 647 (1932).
(6) The antineuritic vitamin. I. The method of assay, concentration of the vitamin with silver under various conditions, and its solubility in certain organic solvents. Ibid., 94, 765 (1932). With G. R. Cowgill and B. H. Klotz.
(7) The antineuritic vitamin. II. Removal of impurities by oxidizing agents. Ibid., 96, 127 (1932). With G. R. Cowgill.
(8) The antineuritic vitamin. III. Removal of impurities by fractional precipitation. Ibid., 97, 421 (1932). With G. R. Cowgill.
(9) The metabolism of cystine and methionine. Availability of methionine in supplementing a diet deficient in cystine. Ibid., 98, 465 (1932). With R. W. Jackson.
(10) The antineuritic vitamin. IV. Preparation of a highly potent concentrate. Ibid., 98, 637 (1932). With G. R. Cowgill.
(11) Studies on vitamin G (B_2). I. Yeast and liver preparations as a source of vitamin G (B_2). Ibid., 103, 643 (1933). With L. R. Farquhar.
(12) Chemical and immunological investigations on the proteins of the nervous system. Psychiat. Quart., 7, 613 (1933). With E. Brand.
(13) Metabolism of D- and L- methionine. Proc. Soc. Exptl. Biol. Med., 30, 587 (1933). With R. W. Jackson.
(14) New type of continuous extractor. J. Biol. Chem., 100, 537 (1933).
(15) The basic amino acids of keratins. The basic amino acid content of human finger nails and cattle horn. Ibid., 104, 339 (1934).
(16) The basic amino acids of serum proteins. Ibid., 103, 261 (1933).
(17) The basic amino acids of serum proteins. II. Effect of heating to 58 degrees. Ibid., 104, 343 (1934).
(18) The basic amino acids of serum proteins. III. A chemical relationship between serum proteins of various origins. Ibid., 104, 347 (1934). With D. C. Darrow and M. K. Cary.
(19) The basic amino acids of serum proteins (orosins). IV. A chemical relationship between various avian orosins. A note on some proteins of the egg. Ibid., 105, 455 (1934).
(20) The antineuritic vitamin. V. Preparation of a vitamin concentrate suitable for parenteral use. Ibid., 105, 463 (1934). With E. H. Stuart and G. R. Cowgill.

(21) The basic amino acids of three crystalline mammalian hemoglobins. Further evidence for a basic amino acid "anlage" of tissue proteins. Ibid., **105**, 663 (1934).
(22) The effect of dry heat and dilute alkali on the lysine content of casein. Ibid., **105**, 667 (1934). With D. B. Jones and C. E. F. Gersdorff.
(23) The determination of the basic amino acids in small quantities of proteins by the silver precipitation method. Ibid., **106**, 457 (1934).
(24) Nature and origin of proteins. Yale J. Biol. Med., **7**, 235 (1935).
(25) Studies on the vitamin B complex: Further indications for the presence of a third factor. Ibid., **8**, 169, (1935). With R. B. Hubbell.
(26) Basic amino acids of human skin. Proc. Soc. Exptl. Biol. Med., **32**, 1574 (1935).
(27) Cystinuria. IV. Metabolism of homocysteine and homocystine. J. Biol. Chem., **110**, 399 (1935). With E. Brand and G. F. Cahill.
(28) Excretion of follicle-stimulating hormone in urine of mental patients in and past menopause. Proc. Soc. Exptl. Biol. Med., **32**, 1576 (1935). With M. M. Harris, E. Brand, and L. E. Hinsie.
(29) Convenient method for preparation of concentrates of follicle-stimulating hormone from urine. Ibid., **33**, 360 (1935). With E. Brand, M. M. Harris, and L. E. Hinsie.
(30) Does bis-(2-aminoethyl)-disulfide (cystamine) promote growth in the rat limited to an inadequate intake of cystine and methionine? J. Biol. Chem., **113**, 135 (1936). With R. W. Jackson.
(31) Carboxymethylcysteine metabolism, its implications on therapy in cystinuria and on the methionine-cysteine relationship. Proc. Soc. Exptl. Biol. Med., **35**, 501 (1936). With E. Brand, B. Kassell, and G. F. Cahill.
(32) Cystinuria. V. Metabolism of casein and lactalbumin. J. Biol. Chem., **119**, 669 (1937). With E. Brand, B. Kassell, and G. F. Cahill.
(33) Cystinuria. VI. Metabolism of the hydroxy analog of methionine (DL-α-hydroxy-γ-methiobutyric acid.) Ibid., **119**, 681, (1937). With E. Brand and G. F. Cahill.
(34) Cystinuria. VII. Metabolism of S-methylcysteine, of γ-thiobutyric acid, and of γ-dithiobutyric acid. Ibid., **119**, 689 (1937). With E. Brand and C. F. Cahill.
(35) Chemical studies on the neuroproteins. I. Amino acid composition of various mammalian brain proteins. Ibid., **119**, 765 (1937).
(36) Chemical studies on the neuroproteins. II. Effect of age on the amino acid composition of human and mammalian brain proteins. Ibid., **120**, 467 (1937).
(37) The basic amino acids of keratins. Basic amino acid content of porcupine quills and echidna spines. Ibid., **121**, 99 (1937). With M. K. Horwitt.
(38) Chemical studies on the neuroproteins. III. An indication for sex differences in the amino acid composition of primate brain proteins. Ibid., **121**, 411 (1937).
(39) Chemical studies on the neuroproteins. IV. Nature of the proteins of the ectoderm: eukeratins and pseudokeratins. Ibid., **121**, 761 (1937).
(40) Proteins of the nervous system, considered in the light of the prevailing hypotheses on protein structure. Yale J. Biol. Med., **9**, 445 (1937).
(41) Comparative biochemistry of the proteins. Cold Spring Harbor Symp. Quant. Biol. **6**, 79 (1938).
(42) Chemical constitution of the proteins. pp. 278-333 in "The Chemistry of the Amino Acids and Proteins," C. L. A. Schmidt, ed., 1031 pp., Charles C. Thomas, Springfield, Ill., 1938.
(43) The metabolism of cystine and methionine. II. Availability of D- and L-methionine and their formyl derivatives in the promotion of growth. J. Biol. Chem., **122**, 425 (1938). With R. W. Jackson.

(44) Estimation of histidine. Proc. Soc. Exptl. Biol. Med., 37, 580 (1937).
(45) The amino acid composition of keratins. Composition of gorgonin, spongin, turtle scutes, and other keratins. J. Biol. Chem., 127, 685 (1939). With D. Bolling.
(46) The composition of keratins. Amino acid composition of hair, wool, horn, and other eukeratins. Ibid., 128, 181 (1939). With cooperation of D. Bolling, F. C. Brand, and A. Schein.
(47) Determination of threonine. Proc. Soc. Exptl. Biol. Med., 40, 710 (1939). With D. Bolling.
(48) Chemical and metabolic studies on phenylalanine. I. Nitration of phenylalanine. J. Biol. Chem., 129, 1 (1939). With D. Bolling.
(49) Microestimation of threonine. Ibid., 130, 365 (1939). With D. Bolling.
(50) Microestimation of leucine, isoleucine, and valine. Proc. Soc. Exptl. Biol. Med., 45, 289 (1940). With D. Bolling and A. A. Kondritzer.
(51) Estimation of histidine. J. Biol. Chem., 133, 67 (1940).
(52) Basic amino acid content of human serum proteins. Influence of the ingestion of arginine on the composition of the serum proteins. Ibid., 133, 71 (1940).
(53) Chemical and metabolic studies on phenylalanine. II. Phenylalanine content of the blood and spinal fluid in phenylpyruvic oligophrenia. Ibid., 134, 105 (1940). With G. A. Jervis, D. Bolling, and E. Kanze.
(54) Chemical and metabolic studies on phenylalanine. III. Amino acid content of tissue proteins of normal and phenylpyruvic oligophrenic individuals. Estimation of phenylalanine. Ibid., 134, 567 (1940). With G. A. Jervis, D. Bolling, and M. Webb.
(55) New method for separation of the basic amino acids from protein hydrolysates. Proc. Soc. Exptl. Biol. Med., 51, 252 (1942).
(56) Amino acids yielded by β-lactoglobulin. Arch. Biochem., 2, 93 (1943). With D. Bolling.
(57) Amino acid yield from various animal and plant proteins after hydrolysis of fat-free tissue. Ibid., 3, 217 (1943). With D. Bolling.
(58) Essential amino acid requirements of man. Yale J. Biol. Med., 15, 723 (1943).
(59) The chemical constitution of the proteins. pp. 1089-1103 in "Addendum to the Chemistry of the Amino Acids and Protein Inclusive of Some of the Advances since 1937." C. L. A. Schmidt, ed., Charles C. Thomas, Springfield, Ill., 1943.
(60) Nutritional opportunities with amino acids. J. Am. Dietet. Assoc., 20, 69 (1944). With D. Bolling.
(61) Comparative analytical study of meat extension. Ibid., 20, 50 (1944). With D. Melnick, H. W. Himes, and B. L. Oser.
(62) Essential amino acid distribution in a casein hydrolysate suitable for parenteral injection. Am. J. Pharm., 116, 368 (1944). With D. Bolling.
(63) Amino acids yielded by yeast, sunflower seed meal, and sesame seed after hydrolysis of the fat-free tissue. Arch. Biochem., 6, 277 (1945). With D. Bolling.
(64) Constitution of salmin. I. Amino acid composition. Ibid., 6, 419 (1945). With D. Bolling.
(65) Amino acid composition of food proteins. Advan. Protein Chem., 2, 119 (1945).
(66) Amino acids yielded by various yeasts after hydrolysis of fat-free material. A comparative investigation. Arch. Biochem., 7, 313 (1945). With D. Bolling.
(67) Amino acid composition of proteins and foods. Science, 103, 431 (1946). With D. Bolling.

(68) Amino acids of cataractous and sclerosed human lenses. Arch. Biochem., 10, 277 (1946). With P. W. Salit.
(69) Effects of baking and toasting on nutritional value of proteins. Ibid., 10, 295 (1946). With P. R. Cannon, R. W. Wissler, C. H. Steffee, R. L. Straube, L. E. Frazier, and R. L. Woolridge.
(70) Amino acid composition of cow and human milk proteins. Ibid., 10, 359 (1946). With D. Bolling.
(71) New method for the preparation of basic amino acid concentrates from protein hydrolyzates. Ibid., 11, 235 (1946).
(72) Chemical and biological properties of tryptic digests of casein and lactalbumin. Ibid., 13, 323 (1947). With D. Bolling and B. F. Chow.
(73) Isolation and synthesis of the naturally occurring α-amino acids. Chem. Revs., 38, 501 (1946).
(74) Some relationships between the amino acid contents of proteins and their nutritive values for the rat. J. Biol. Chem., 163, 599 (1946). With H. H. Mitchell.
(75) Correlation of the amino acid composition of proteins with their nutritive value. Nutrition Abstr. and Rev., 16, 249 (1946). With H. H. Mitchell.
(76) Detection of sulfur-containing amino acids on paper chromatograms. Science, 108, 506 (1948). With H. M. Winegard and G. Toennies.
(77) Quantitative estimation of amino acids on paper chromatograms. Ibid., 108, 608 (1948).
(78) Preparation and amino acid composition of salmin and clupein. Proc. Soc. Exptl. Biol. Med., 70, 494 (1949). With D. Bolling, H. Gershon, and H. A. Sober.
(79) Quantitative paper chromatography: A simplified procedure. Ibid., 72, 337 (1949).
(80) Separation of amino acids by ion exchange chromatography. pp. 295-314 in "Ion Exchange Theory and Application," F. C. Nachod, ed., 411 pp., Academic press, Inc., New York, 1949.
(81) Biological studies on the value of dietary supplements of milk and milk products. J. Am. Dietet. Assoc., 25, 937 (1949).
(82) Comparative protein chemistry. The composition of the proteins of human teeth and fish scales. J. Dental Res., 28, 518 (1949). With M. K. Horwitt and D. Bolling.
(83) Paper chromatograms spot amino acids. Two-dimensional microseparation patterns quickly identify them—or other substances—in a mixture. Added tests give concentrations. Food Ind., 22, 824-951 (1950).
(84) Estimation of amino acids and amines on paper chromatograms. Anal. Chem., 22, 1327 (1950).
(85) Paper chromatography of amino acids. pp. 181-200 in "Colloid Chemistry; Theoretical and Applied," Vol. 8, J. Alexander, ed., 736 pp., Reinhold, New York, 1950. With H. A. Sober.
(86) Synthesis of sulfur amino acids from inorganic sulfate by ruminants. Proc. Soc. Exptl. Biol. Med., 73, 391 (1950). With J. A. Stekol.
(87) Amino acids in posterior pituitary protein. Nature, 165, 975 (1950). With H. B. van Dyke.
(88) Quantities of amino acids in nonprotein fraction of breast and cow's milk. Arch. Biochem., 25, 350 (1950). With D. Bolling.
(89) Comparative study on two samples of neurokeratin. Arch. Biochem. Biophys., 31, 266 (1950).
(90) Some amino acids, peptides, and amines in milk, concentrated milks, and cheese. J. Dairy Sci., 34, 1 (1951).

(91) Chemical classification of keratins. J. Soc. Cosmetic Chemists, 2, 235 (1951).
(92) Synthesis of sulfur amino acids from inorganic sulfate by ruminants. II. Synthesis of cystine and methionine from sodium sulfate by the goat and by the microorganisms of the rumen of the ewe. Arch. Biochem. Biophys., 33, 353 (1951). With J. A. Stekol and J. K. Loosli.
(93) The nutrient materials in food, pp. 25-75, in "Food for Life," R. W. Gerard, ed., 306 pp. University of Chicago Press, Chicago, Ill., 1952.
(94) Amino acids in posterior pituitary protein. Arch Biochem. Biophys., 36, 1 (1952). With H. B. van Dyke.
(95) Effect of heat treatment on the sulfhydryl groups in skim milk and non-fat dry milk. J. Dairy Sci., 36, 427 (1953). With G. Zweig.
(96) Studies on bovine whey proteins. I. Preparation of ferric derivatives of whey proteins. Arch. Biochem. Biophys., 47, 88 (1953). With D. Bolling, K. W. Weiss, and G. Zweig.
(97) Studies on bovine whey proteins. II. Removal of iron from ferric derivatives of whey proteins. Ibid., 48, 386 (1954). With G. Zweig.
(98) Experiments with ion-selective membranes. I. Electrolytic deionization of protein-free whey. J. Dairy Sci., 37, 932 (1954). With W. H. Winegard.
(99) Simplified procedure for measuring cellulose digestion by rumen microorganisms. Contribs. Boyce Thompson Inst., 17, 337 (1954). With R. Henderson and F. E. Hervat.
(100) Quantitative amino acid composition of the German cockroach, Blatella germanica (L.). Ibid., 17, 380 (1954). With J. D. Hilchey.
(101) Studies on bovine whey proteins. IV. Amino acid analyses of crystalline β-lactoglobulins and lactalbumin by quantitative paper chromatography. Arch. Biochem. Biophys., 55, 315 (1955). With K. W. Weiss.
(102) Sulfur metabolism of insects. I. Utilization of sulfate for formation of cystine and methionine by the German cockroach, Blatella germanica (L.). Contribs. Boyce Thompson Inst., 18, 109 (1955). With J. D. Hilchey, L. P. Miller, and R. M. Weed.
(103) Amino acids. Encyclopedia Americana, 1, 575 (1955).
(104) Amino acid composition of southern bean mosaic virus. Contribs. Boyce Thompson Inst., 18, 371 (1956). With Beatrice S. Magdoff and Diane Block Montie.
(105) Effect of long-time feeding of a soybean infant food diet to white rats. Ann. Allergy, 14, 166 (1956). With H. W. Howard, D. W. Anderson, and C. D. Bauer. Bauer.
(106) Protein requirements of animals including man. Borden's Rev. Nutr. Res., 17, 75 (1956).
(107) Effect of supplementing soybean proteins with lysine and other amino acids. A. M. A. J. Diseases Children, 92, 126 (1956). With D. W. Anderson, H. W. Howard, and C. D. Bauer.
(108) Comparative study of amino acid composition of commercial samples of a high-protein and a low protein and a low-protein wheat flour. Contribs. Boyce Thompson Inst., 18, 477 (1957). With R. H. Mandl.
(109) Pathogenesis of congenital goiter and abnormally high levels of SPI and with mono- and diiodotyrosine in the serum. J. Clin. Endocrinol. Metabolism, 17, 817 (1957). With S. C. Werner, R. H. Mandl, and A. A. H. Kassenaar.
(110) Circulating iodoproteins in a nongoitrous adult with primary amenorrhea, body deformities, and normal levels of serum precipitable iodine and thyroidal I^{131} intake. Ibid., 17, 1141 (1957). With S. C. Werner and R. H. Mandl.
(111) Nutritive value of bread flour proteins as affected by practical supplementation with lactalbumin, nonfat dry milk solids, soybean proteins, wheat

gluten, and lysine. J. Nutrition, **64**, 151 (1958). With H. W. Howard, W. J. Monson, and C. D. Bauer.
(112) Nitrogen requirements of animals and man. Comments on the Folin and Schoenheimer hypotheses. Proc. Intern. Symposium on Enzyme Chem., Tokyo and Kyoto, 1957, 444 (1958).
(113) Amino acid composition of bread proteins. J. Am. Dietet. Assoc., **34**, 724 (1958). With R. H. Mandl.
(114) Sulfur metabolism of yeast. I. Study of relative growth of five yeasts on a sulfur-free medium supplemented with small quantities of sulfur compound. Contribs. Boyce Thompson Inst., **19**, 437 (1958). With D. Margolis.
(115) Amino acid composition of serum proteins. I. Fractionation of bovine serum proteins by ammonium sulfate and comparative amino acid composition of the fractions. Ibid., **19**, 445 (1958). With S. Keller.
(116) Amino acid composition of the serum proteins. II. Fractionation of human serum proteins by cellulose ion-exchange chromatography and comparative amino acid composition of the fractions. Ibid., **19**, 451 (1958). With S. Keller.
(117) Method for investigation of the distribution of radioiodine in the serum after small test doses of 1^{131}. Arch. Biochem. Biophys., **73**, 9 (1958).
(118) Binding of mixtures of iodoamino acids and of inorganic iodide by various serum proteins. Ibid., **75**, 508 (1958). With R. H. Mandl and S. Keller.
(119) Approximate amino acid composition of wild and hatchery trout (Salvelinus fontinalis) and some of their principal foods (Grammarus and Hexagenia bilineata). Contribs. Boyce Thompson Inst., **20**, 103 (1959).
(120) Nutritive value of commercial breads. J. Am. Dietet. Assoc., **35**, 345 (1959) With H. W. Howard, W. J. Monson, and C. D. Bauer.
(121) Methods for qualitative, semiquantitative, and quantitative determination of iodoamino acids and of inorganic iodide in iodoprotein digests and in human serum. Arch. Biochem. Biophys., **81**, 25 (1959). With R. H. Mandl.
(122) Discrepancy between distribution of iodine in human serum when estimated by iodine-131 and iodine-127. Nature, **183**, 406 (1959). With S. C. Werner.
(123) Chemical relationship between the protein fractions obtained from fowl serum by cellulose ion-exchange chromatography. Evidence for amino acid "anlage." Arch. Biochem. Biophys., **83**, 426 (1959). With S. Keller and D. W. Meller.
(124) Amino acid composition of serum proteins. III. Chromatographic isolation of human and bovine serum albumins, and amino acid composition of the fractions. Ibid., **85**, 366 (1959). With S. Keller.
(125) Separation of Proteins, pp. 1-30 in "A Laboratory Manual of Analytical Methods of Protein Chemistry," Vol. 1, 254 pp., Pergamon Press, London, 1960. With S. Keller.
(126) Fractionation of proteins by absorption and ion exchange. Part A, pp. 67-87 in "A Laboratory Manual of Analytical Methods of Protein Chemistry," P. Alexander and R. J. Block, eds., Vol. 1, 254 pp., Pergamon Press, London, 1960. With S. Keller.
(127) Sulfur metabolism of insects. IV. Conversion of inorganic sulfate to organic sulfur compounds in cockroaches. Role of intracellular symbionts. Contribs. Boyce Thompson Inst., **20**, 317 (1960). With S. M. Henry.
(128) Sulfur metabolism of insects. V. Ability of insects to use sulfate in synthesis of methionine. Ibid., **20**, 363 (1960). With T. H. Haines and S. M. Henry.
(129) Probable genetic basis for abnormal circulating iodoproteins (butanol-insoluble serum iodine). Study of a family with several hypothyroid members with and without goiter. J. Clin. Endocrinol. Metabolism, **20**, 205 (1960). With S. C. Werner and R. H. Mandl.

(130) Probable presence of diiodotyrosine and of moniodotyrosine in human serum. Discrepancy between the distribution of iodo compounds when estimated by I^{131} and I^{127}. Arch Biochem. Biophys., **88**, 98 (1960). With S. C. Werner, R. H. Mandl, V. V. Row, and I. Radichevich.

(131) Methods of increasing the nutritive value of foods. B. Addition of amino acids. pp. 508-520 in "Nutritional Evalutaion of Food Processing," 612 pp., Robert S. Harris and Harry von Loesecke, eds., 612 pp., Wiley, New York, 1960.

(132) Dietary protein values. Complete vs. total protein in the evaluation of diets. J. Agr. Food Chem., **8**, 486 (1960). With H. W. Howard and C. D. Bauer.

(133) Amino acid analysis of protein hydrolysates. pp. 1-57 in "A Laboratory Manual of Analytical Methods of Protein Chemistry," P. Alexander and R. J. Block, eds., Vol. 2, 518 pp., Pergamon Press, London, 1960.

(134) Interrelationships between serum protein fractions isolated by various techniques. Evidence for amino acid anlagen. Contribs. Boyce Thompson Inst., **20**, 385 (1960). With S. Keller.

(135) Sulfur metabolism of insects. VI. Metabolism of the sulfur amino acids and related compounds in the German cockroach, Blatella Germanica (L.). Ibid., **21**, 129 (1961). With S. M. Henry.

(136) Metabolism of the sulfur amino acids and of sulfate in Blatella Germanica. Nature, **191**, 392 (1961). With S. M. Henry.

(137) Curative action of iodine on soybean goiter and the changes in the distribution of iodoamino acids in the serum and in thyroid gland digests. Arch. Biochem. Biophys., **93**, 15 (1961). With R. H. Mandl, H. W. Howard, C. D. Bauer, and D. W. Anderson.

(138) Comment on "Effects of soybean product on thyroid function in humans." pp. 338-339 in "Year Book of Pediatrics, 1960-1961 Series," Gellid, ed., Medical Publishing Co., 1961. With D. W. Anderson and H. W. Howard.

(139) Chromatography paper. pp. 228-230 in "The Encyclopedia of the Biological Sciences," P. Gray, ed., 1119 pp. Reinhold, New York, 1961.

(140) Amino acid interrelationships between the various serum proteins obtained by salting out, electrophoresis, and column chromatography. Ann. N. Y. Acad. Sci., **94**, 31 (1961).

(141) Puromycin-induced changes in uredospores of Puccinia sorghi Schw. Science, **134**, 739 (1961). With R. C. Staples and R. Syamananda.

(142) Distribution of I^{131} and I^{127} in sera of patients with nontoxic nodular goiter. In "Advance in Thyroid Research; Trans. of the 4th Internat. Conf. on Goiter, London, 1960," R. Pitt-Rivers, ed., 2 vols. Pergamon Press, London, 1961. With S. C. Werner, I. Radichevich, V. V. Row, and R. H. Mandl.

(143) Automatic analysis of iodoamino acids in digests of iodinated proteins. Biochem. J., **81**, 37P (1961). With R. H. Mandl.

(144) Sulfur metabolism in algae. I. Synthesis of metabolically inert chloroform-soluble sulfate esters by two chrysomonads and Chlorella pyrenoidesa. J. Protozool., **9**, 33 (1962). With T. H. Haines.

(145) Chromatographic and electrophoretic methods. pp. 165-171 in "The Thyroid," S. C. Werner, ed., 2nd ed., Harper-Hoeber, New York, 1962.

BOOKS

Determination of the Amino Acids. Richard J. Block. 91 pp. Burgess Publishing Co., Minneapolis, Minn., 1938. Revised ed. with Diana Bolling. 58 pp. 1941.
Amino Acid Composition of Proteins and Foods. Analytical Methods and Results.

Richard J. Block and Diana Bolling. 396 pp. Charles C. Thomas, Springfield, Ill., 1945. 2nd ed. 576 pp. 1951.

Paper Chromatography. A Laboratory Manual. Richard J. Block, Raymond LeStrange, and Gunter Zweig. 195 pp. Academic Press, Inc., New York, 1952.

Manual of Paper Chromatography and Paper Electrophoresis. Richard J. Block, Emmett L. Durrum, and Gunter Zweig. 484 pp. Academic Press, Inc., New York, 1955. 2nd ed. 710 pp. 1958.

Amino Acid Handbook. Methods and Results of Protein Analysis. Richard J. Block with cooperation of Kathryn W. Weiss. 386 pp. Charles C. Thomas, Springfield, Ill., 1956.

Laboratory Manual of Analytical Methods of Protein Chemistry (Including Polypeptids). P. Alexander and R. J. Block, eds. Pergamon Press, London. Vol. 1, 254 pp., 1960. Vol. 2, 518 pp., 1960. Vol. 3, 286 pp., 1961.

The Nature and Origin of the Serum Proteins

JULIUS SCHULTZ

*Institute for Biochemical Studies in Cancer,
Department of Biochemistry, Hahnemann Medical
College, Philadelphia, Pa.*

> The contributions of Richard Block to the serum protein problem originated from the hypothesis of Kossel. From recent data on the amino acid composition of the proteins found in animal sera, a formulation is derived which reflects the properties of a continuous system of molecular species originating from a common biosynthetic pathway, as if from mixed polymers of monomeric peptides of lower molecular weight. Indirect evidence of this is found in the amino acid interrelationship, and direct evidence is limited to the isolation of peptides of common composition, whose primary structures are still under investigation. These findings suggest that undifferentiated proteins may be continuous systems rather than discrete molecular species.

The amino acid composition of proteins was one of the major interests of Block's intellectual endeavor. He carried with him a great deal of the biochemical heritage of the Mendel, Osborne, and Vickery school, in which he was well tutored. This school viewed proteins in the light of their amino acid composition.

Physiological Meaning

It was Block's tendency to read as much physiological meaning into an amino acid analysis as his training and experience allowed that led him into the development of a hypothesis concerned with amino acid interrelationship of serum proteins. Although his concepts received some attention in the 30's (graduate students at the University of Michigan were required to read his papers), there are few citations to his work in comprehensive reviews on the plasma proteins, published only a few years ago (31). As the knowledge of the physical chemical properties of proteins grew, the influence of the amino acids on the functional character of the protein was given a minor role. Thus in commenting on H. B. Vickery's statement, "in recent years there has arisen the conviction that not only the chemical but also the physical properties, or at least many of them, can be assigned a rational explanation in terms of the amino acid composition" (45), Bailey argued that "one of the most disheartening features of the amino acid analysis of proteins is that the results have little meaning" (44).

In view of the sudden invasion of the organic chemist's approach to protein structure, the elucidation with explosive force of the primary structure of a number of proteins and active site sequences, and a most recent statement that structure and function may be determined by primary structure (1), one must consider seriously that a given amino acid may play a particularly important role in determining function.

Thus with the re-emergence of the dominant role of the amino acids, envisioned by Vickery, Block returned to the theater and began to replay his part in the investigation of serum proteins of a quarter of a century ago, only to be cut off as a result of an untimely accident.

Anlage Hypothesis

It often takes as much courage to draw a physiologically oriented inference from chemical data based on crude material obtained from experimental animals or patients as to derive these inferences from the data on dead, highly purified chemical entities obtained under rigid physical chemical controls. Thus when Block determined the basic amino acids arginine, lysine, and histidine in the albumin and globulin fractions of patients whose albumin-globulin (A/G) ratios varied, he found that, in spite of the marked variation of the proportion of the two protein fractions, the molar ratios of the bases remained constant (4, 8). This was like analyzing a series of mixtures of alkali phosphates; regardless of the proportions of Na to K to H, the ratio of P to O would remain 1 to 4. In this respect the PO_4 determines the principal properties of the mixtures; likewise, with great enthusiasm Block assumed that the determiners here were the basic amino acids, the "anlage," which Kossel in 1905 (21) called protamin, a basic protein. So with a strong tendency toward "reading into" the amino acid data, he proposed that the serum proteins were one great molecule from which all isolated products were obtained as a result of chemical treatment. In the work of Sorensen (43) and Hardy (15) Block found physical chemical support of this notion.

Block ignored the brilliant investigations taking place in Cohn's laboratory at Harvard, where a multitude of purified plasma protein fractions were being isolated, because chemical reagents were used in the process. But when Tiselius provided a means of demonstrating the existence of a number of serum electrophoretic components with a minimal exposure of the serum to chemical reagents, Block gave up. For about 20 years he lost interest in the subject and published nothing. Brand's analysis of the Cohn fractions offered no support for his hypothesis (9, 10). In the late 50's, following the development of paper chromatographic procedures for the amino acids, to which he contributed (6), and chromatography for separation of proteins, he renewed his interest and produced a series of papers which were reviewed in an address before the New York Academy of Sciences (3).

With these newer methods of protein separation and amino acid analysis he prepared serum protein fractions by serial salting out with ammonium sulfate and by the Sober and Peterson DEAE cellulose columns (42), using the sera of reptile, fowl, and mammalian blood. Some of the amino acid analyses were carried out by the automatic amino acid methods of Hirs, Moore, and Stein (18). Fortified with this plethora of data, Block now had the opportunity to re-examine not only the ratio of the basic amino acids, but at least 12 amino acids in a variety of protein fractions prepared by at least two different procedures. With the aid of a statistician he determined the significance of the constancy of the molar ratios of pairs of amino acids and found that in spite of the marked variation of the absolute amounts of an amino acid, the molar ratios of certain pairs remain relatively constant among the numerous protein components of animal sera.

Fourteen of the 18 amino acids analyzed were found to have relatively constant molar ratios, with two other amino acids at the 1% level, and a less than 10% deviation from the mean molar ratios. Block repeated these findings from each species and from proteins obtained by the two methods of preparation. As a check on the validity of the statistics he presented to the statistician the determination of amino acid in eight apparently unrelated proteins: bovine serum albumin, human hemoglobin, crystalline egg albumin, insulin, β-lactoglobulin, actin, gelatin, and ribonuclease. The statistician, led to believe that these were eight protein fractions of the serum, reported 105 pairs; only five pairs were significantly related at the 1% level and three pairs were actually negatively correlated. This is expected by chance. In contrast were the results obtained from a series of proteins of chicken serum, for example, where there were also 105 pairs; 26 were correlated at the 5% level of significance. To summarize Block's most recent conception of the serum proteins in his own words (3):

> These findings suggest that all serum proteins are composed of amino acid anlagen—that is, a limited number of different peptides, each of which has a relatively constant amino acid content but differs from the others in amino acid composition.

Block's results appear to support the concept that the proteins of the serum are not a mixture of various unrelated proteins, but the protein fractions, whether homogeneous or not, are interrelated and may exist as a complex of easily dissociable molecules that he had named orosin in 1934 (5).

In essence the development of the anlage hypothesis arose from Kossel's use of an embryological term as applied to protamine as a basic unit of protein structure, which Block in the 1930's translated into the constancy of the arg-lys-his ratio in the serum proteins. He changed this in his most recent suggestion that this anlage was represented by yet to be found common peptides. No matter what one may think of the conceptual implications of such data from Kossel's time to the present, the fact remains that the serum proteins appear to be more closely interrelated than is currently taught or thought in biochemistry today, where albumin, alpha-1-, alpha-2-, beta-, and gamma-globulins as seen in Tiselius' patterns, the 18 column fractions of Sober and Peterson (42), and the multicomponent systems of gel electrophoretic components of Smithies (41) are usually treated as discrete individuals or mixtures of proteins, and discussion of any interrelationship has only very recently been indicated in the case of the gamma-globulins (2, 13). In some reviews, such as the two volumes of "Plasma Proteins," such interrelations have not been recognized, except to speculate that the gamma-globulin may be a family of proteins (32), without reference to Block's work.

It is possible that in the future we may recognize Kossel's idea of the anlage, a basic protein determiner found in all cells, to be the modern-day equivalent of the "coat" or "masking" protein which actually determines the particular areas of the DNA (deoxyribonucleic acid) molecule which are to function in RNA (ribonucleic acid) formation in a given cell—that is, Kossel's anlage may be the intellectual antecedent of the principle of cellular differentiation as viewed by many today. On the other hand, if such kindness to our predecessors is to be extended to the ideas of Richard Block, who transformed Kossel's anlage first to the basic amino acids (7) and then to "common peptides," it can easily be said that the concept of the common active site sequence of many enzymes (20) is what Block meant when he inferred that a "peptide" anlage determined the function of many proteins.

As far as the serum proteins are concerned, no one has yet isolated peptides whose sequence of amino acids from more than one component of the serum is identical. The significance of this search is discussed in the remainder of this presentation.

Biosynthesis of Serum Proteins

The present author's line of research crossed that of Block in the author's attempt to determine criteria other than mobility to distinguish proteins responsible for alterations of the gaussian envelopes of the classical Tiselius electrophoretic patterns of the serum proteins found in tumor-bearing rats (38). In these experiments, when six amino acids were determined on the electrophoretic fractions obtained by starch slab electrophoresis of dog, rat, and human sera, certain relations became evident, which gave rise to a speculation as to the mode of biosynthesis of the serum proteins (36, 37). This hypothesis depended on the demonstration of the presence of common peptides in the proteins of the serum. In view of the fact that even acellular systems of protein biosynthesis so remarkably illuminated by recent investigators (28) do not yield single proteins on the addition of given polynucleotide from a natural source, it is evident that a series or a system of proteins may be produced from a given site, whether this takes place directly on the site itself or peptides from the template appear as monomers which

1. SCHULTZ The Nature and Origin of the Serum Proteins

are reformed into mixed polymeric macromolecules. Nevertheless proteins of the serum synthesized in the liver (26) do have the characteristics of a system; in addition, they are without specific enzymatic function and are therefore undifferentiated. In this way the serum proteins may serve as a physiological model for the matrix products of the messenger RNA of the hepatic parenchymal cell. This approach, in

Table I. Chemical Relationships among 16 Isolated Electrophoretic Components of Sera of Dog, Rat, and Man (37)

Molar Ratio	No. of Proteins Included [a]	Range
(Ala + gly)/asp	16	1.3—1.5
Glu/ala	14 [b]	1.3—1.5
Thr/asp	16	0.5—0.6

[a] Gamma-globulins excluded.
[b] Alpha-2, rat = 1.1
  Albumin, dog = 1.6.

Table II. Molar Ratios of Amino Acids Characteristic of Serum Proteins Compared to Proteins of Other Sources

Proteins	Ala+Gly / Asp	Glu / Ala	Thr / Asp	Ref.
Serum	(1.3—1.5)	(1.3—1.5)	(0.5—0.6)	(Table I)
Myokinase	3.0	3.0	1.2	(23)
ATP creatine PO_4 kinase	1.3	3.0	0.6	(29)
Cytochrome c	2.2	2.0	1.2	(24)
LDH	1.4	1.5	0.4	(25)
Hemoglobin				
α-chain	2.3	0.2	0.8	(17)
β-chain	2.1	0.7	0.5	(17)
Tryptophan-synthetase	3.0	0.8	0.4	(16)
Rat albumin	1.5	1.3	0.6	(30)
Pancreatic protein				
Trypsinogen	1.8	0.8	0.5	(27)
Chymotrypsinogen B	2.0	0.6	1.1	(19)
Ribonuclease	1.1	1.0	0.7	(18)
Carboxypeptidase	1.4	1.2	0.9	(40)
Egg proteins				
Ovalbumin	1.7	1.5	0.6	(22)
Lysozyme	0.7	0.5	0.3	(22)
Conalbumin	1.25	1.6	0.5	(22)
Ovomucoid	0.8	1.7	0.5	(22)
Histones				
A	15.1	0.2	2.7	(12)
B	3.6	0.7	0.9	(12)
C	8.0	0.3	1.7	(12)

addition to the efforts of Šorm (44) in searching for areas of common sequences among the highly differentiated proteins of specific function, may contribute to understanding some of the steps between the raw template material and the end product.

While Block's interest was centered on the constancy of the molar ratio of certain pairs of amino acids, we were concerned not only with that parameter (Tables I and II) but also with the observation that the molar ratios of other pairs varied systematically with the mobility of the particular protein fraction (Figure 1). Since one might expect this

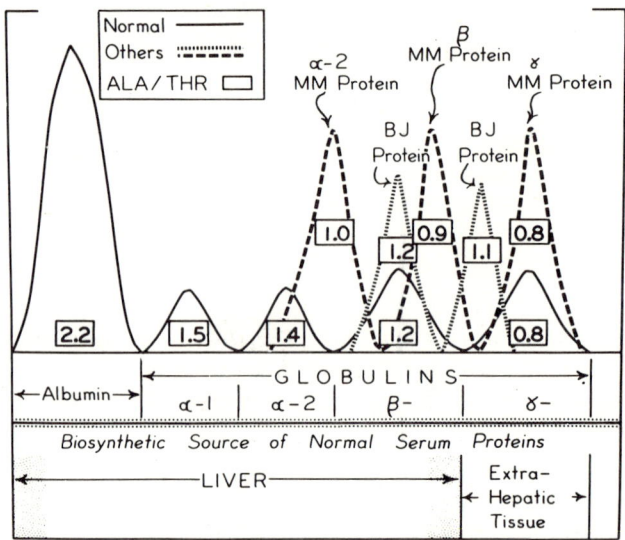

Figure 1. Systematic variation of molar ratio of ala to thr with mobility of electrophoretic components of serum proteins

to be true of certain amino acids such as lysine, arginine, or the dicarboxylic acids, which, because of their excess charge, contribute heavily to the more basic or acidic proteins, we chose alanine and threonine, neither of which would be characteristic of the lower or faster moving proteins because of their electrical properties, per se. The observation that alanine and threonine varied systematically was first seen in our single-dimensional amino acid chromatograms of the five electrophoretic components, published in 1955 (37).

Figure 1 shows diagrammatically the arrangement of the proteins of the serum in accordance with their mobilities, as would be found in a classical electrophoretical pattern obtained by electrophoresis of normal serum at pH 8.6 in veronal buffer. The Bence-Jones and myeloma globulins are also placed in areas where they were found in respect to the serum proteins indicated (see Table V for other data on these proteins). In each system, in both the hepatic and extrahepatic proteins (26), the ala-thr ratios change in the same direction as the mobility, although these amino acids themselves do not significantly contribute to the electrical properties of the proteins, but in this may be associated with an acidic peptide common to each protein but increasing in proportion to other peptides with increasing mobility of the component (see Table II for the relatively constant ala-glu ratio in all proteins of the serum).

The fact that certain pairs of amino acids were constant regardless of mobility, and others were characteristic of proteins of a given mobility, gave rise to the thought that there were common features suggestive of a system of interwoven units. The rationale for this was relatively simple.

If a series of peptides is synthesized from the long template site, and these products are organized into proteins consisting of various proportions of these products, the mixture of proteins formed should have certain inherent features which would distinguish them from a similar mixture formed from another template site. Thus, a series of three peptides, A, B, and C, from a template could be chosen so that B is more acid than A, and C is more basic than A. The mobility of a

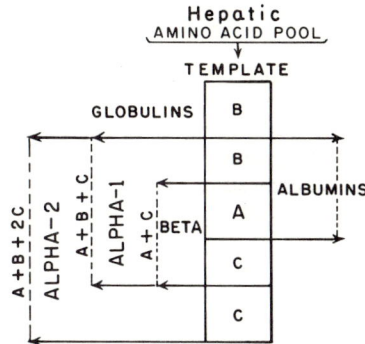

Figure 2. Proposed mechanism of biosynthesis of animal serum proteins. A, B, C are positions on template available for certain groups of amino acids; the arrows indicate the resultant proteins after assembly on the ribosomes.

protein made up of these peptides would be a function of A plus the ratio of B/C. On electrophoresis, the Tiselius pattern of the mixture of proteins derived from this particular template would provide a series of proteins whose composition would reflect components A, B, and C in a manner that would distinguish the family from a similar series arising from another template or other templates.

To test this hypothesis, the only method available in the early 50's was a crude approximation arrived at by tabulating all the amino acid values in terms of molar ratios of aspartic acid, and from the 16 protein components of dog, rat, and man assembling the lowest ratio for each amino acid into a hypothetical peptide representing A. Since the values of alanine and glutamic acid increased with increasing mobility of the component, but remained in constant molar ratio to each other, they were said to be characteristic of peptide B; in like manner, since glycine and serine values increased with decreasing mobility of the components, they were assigned to the C peptide. As we had seen with the ala-thr ratios, the ratios of B/(B+C), called n/K, were remarkably characteristic of the mobility of each of the electrophoretic components of the sera of dog, rat, and man [Table III and (37)].

Table III. Formulation Interrelating Serum Proteins

Component	B	C	n/K
Albumin	117	0	1.0
Alpha-1	37	36	0.5
Alpha-2	28	56	0.33
Beta	2	72	0.03
Gamma	20	138	0.13

It has been shown (37) that the minimal molar ratios per 100 moles of aspartic acid found in the 16 proteins prepared by starch electrophoresis of the sera of dog, rat, and man were: glu 90, ala 70, thr 50, ser 40, and gly 30. This represented the hypothetical A peptide. When these ratios were subtracted from the values of the molar ratio of each amino acid from each protein, the values given in Table III were found. Peptide B is represented by the excess number of moles of ala plus glu, which equals n in Equation 1; peptide C is represented by the values from excess gly plus ser. The sum of these two values for each protein is equal to K, and

$$\mu = f[A + nB + (K - n)C] \tag{1}$$

Since A has been subtracted from each protein, the mobility becomes a function of the n/K ratio, as seen in the figures of the last column of Table III. n/K values will not correspond to the mobility in proteins not made up from peptide units arising from another site of synthesis, as indicated here by the gamma-globulins, which apparently arise from a different system (Figure 1).

Together with the criteria set by the pairs of amino acids whose molar ratios were constant, the n/K ratios offered distinguishing features that characterized the system found in the serum from other proteins picked at random. This would be expected, because while the total aspartic and glutamic acids may provide the principal source of negativity, other proteins may contain the two amino acids in differing proportions, and the alanine would not necessarily be in the same ratio to glutamic acid as is found in all of the serum proteins. Figure 2 shows diagrammatically the template site and the possible manner in which a system of proteins might be assembled to satisfy the data.

In modern terminology the messenger RNA would collect the amino acid of peptides represented by A + B + C, etc., and deposit them on a ribosome where they would be assembled to give rise to A + C, or albumin; AC, β-globulin; and various proportions of B + C in addition to A to give rise to a continuous system. A, B, and C are model peptides, but the system is not necessarily limited to these three, in that these three are not discrete peptides but rather areas on the template; by this mechanism "common peptides" should appear in high incidence among the serum proteins.

Naturally the implication arose that there should be a high incidence of common peptides in the partial hydrolyzates of each of the serum proteins. This, of course, is the same implication that arose in Block's mind (3). Since 1956 this laboratory has been busy trying to isolate common peptides from each of the serum proteins as obtained from electrophoresis on starch slabs. In order to be able to prepare each of the protein hydrolyzates simultaneously we examined nonenzymatic procedures and devised the dilute acid partial hydrolyzate method which has recently been described in detail (33, 34). In this method aspartic acid is preferentially eliminated from the peptide chain, the re-

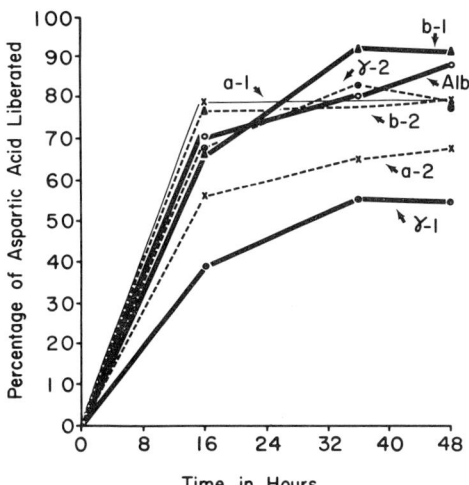

Figure 3. Liberation of aspartic acid during 48-hour partial hydrolysis of each serum protein in 0.03N HCl at 105°C.

Ordinate indicates percentage of total aspartic acid found at time interval shown at abscissa, using aspartic acid value of a 24-hour hydrolysis in 6N HCl as equal to 100 (33, 34)

sulting mixture of peptides is fingerprinted, and the ninhydrin-positive areas are located and eluted. By repeating the mapping procedures many times, sufficient material was accumulated to obtain an amino acid analysis.

Thus in Figures 3 to 8 can be seen the aspartic acid released from each of the proteins under these conditions, along with the values for other amino acids being split at the same time.

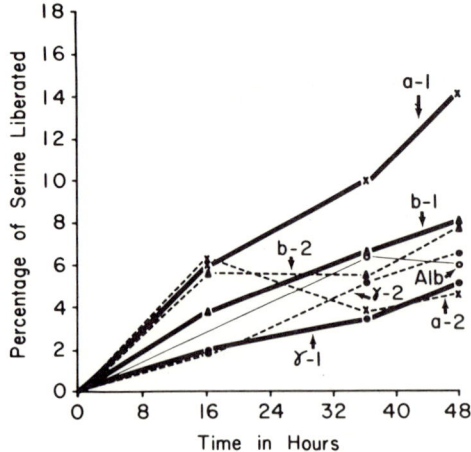

Figure 4. Liberation of serine from serum proteins at 105°C. in 0.03N HCl

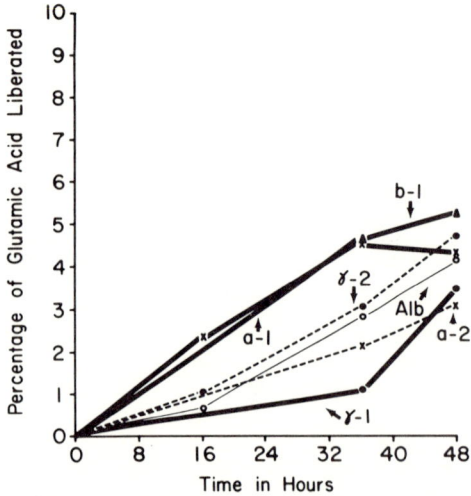

Figure 5. Liberation of glutamic acid from serum proteins at 105°C. in 0.03N HCl

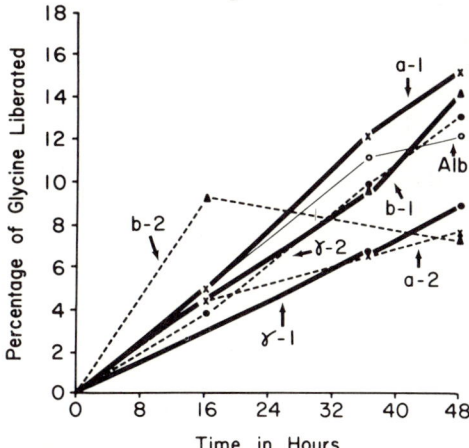

Figure 6. Liberation of glycine from serum proteins at 105°C. in 0.03N HCl

Over 50% of the aspartic acid of the proteins of hepatic origin is liberated in 16 hours, but the gamma-globulins of extrahepatic origin required 36 hours to reach 50%. The extent to which this reflects certain characteristics of the primary structure is described in similar studies on insulin, ribonuclease, and glucagon (37). The cleavage of the peptide chain at the aspartic acid bonds may release other amino acids when they are between aspartic acid residues, when the aspartic acid is penultimate at either end of the chain, or if the other residues occupy positions of particularly labile sequences not known at this time. The

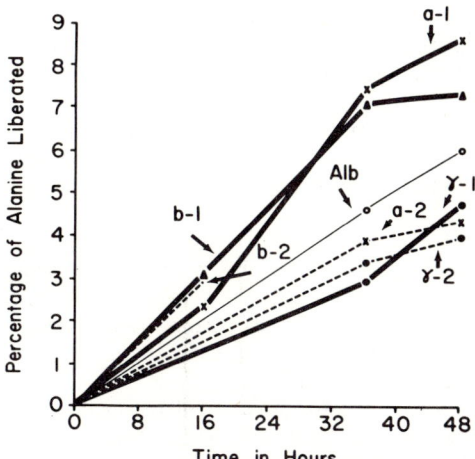

Figure 7. Liberation of alanine from serum proteins at 105°C. in 0.03N HCl.

extent to which all three of these factors are operating is indicated in Figures 4 to 8, where except for glycine, less than 10% liberation takes place in 48 hours, and in all cases less than 5% in 16 hours. In most cases free amino acids are liberated from gamma-globulins at a lower rate than the other serum proteins.

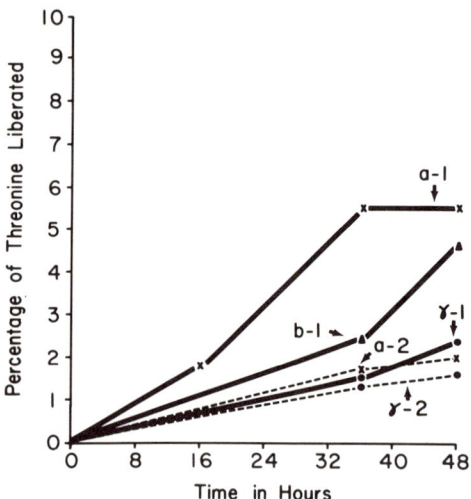

Figure 8. Liberation of threonine from serum proteins at 105°C. in 0.03N HCl

Figure 9 shows the peptide maps and Table IV the amino acid compositions of some of the peptides.

Following hydrolysis in 0.03N HCl at 105° C., the solution of the cleaved protein is evaporated to remove the acid, and taken up in a small volume of water. A suitable aliquot, usually containing 7.5 µg. of α-amino nitrogen, is electrophoresed in 0.1 N formic acid at 10 to 12 kv. across 100-cm.-long Whatman No. 1 paper, 8 inches wide, for 15 to 20 minutes with the Gilson Medical Electronics Electrophorator. A section 20 cm. from the origin is cut, and the 20 × 8 inch piece is chromatographed in butanol-acetic acid-water (3:1:1) at 60° C. for 90 minutes.

After drying, the paper, stained with ninhydrin, appears as indicated in Figure 9. Aspartic acid is in the heavy spot closest to the origin. With light staining and using the above as templates, one can repeat these runs, elute the spots, and examine them further. Spots 7 and 8 have been studied in more detail than the others; all on elution and acid hydrolysis give rise to amino acids.

The analysis, using an automatic amino acid analyzer (Phoenix), of spots 7 and 8 is shown in Table IV. These spots were eluted from the peptide maps of each partial acid hydrolyzate and hydrolyzed in 6N HCl for 24 hours at 105°C. before being placed on the automatic amino acid analyzer. Each value is the moles of amino acid indicated per mole of

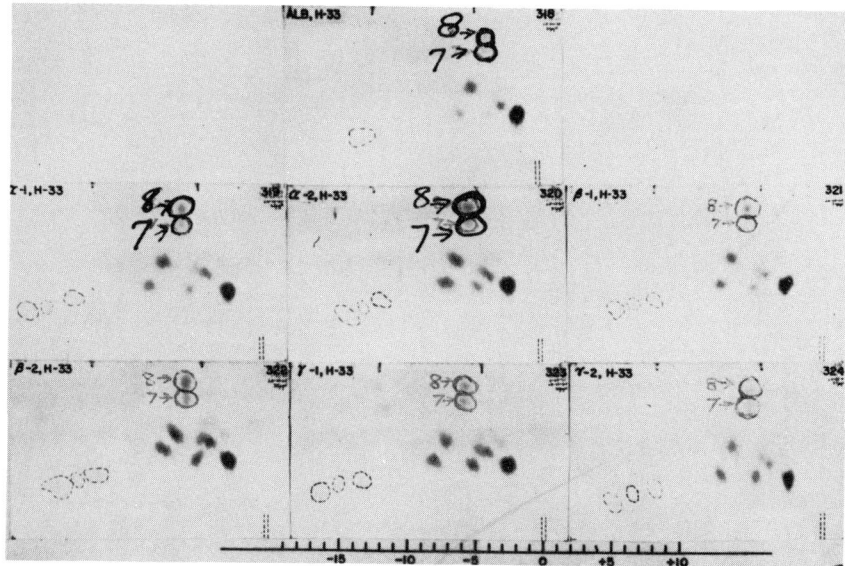

Figure 9. Peptide maps of partial acid hydrolyzates of serum proteins described in text and Figures 3 to 8

serine found. It is possible that a peptide of composition ser, thr, glu, gly, val, ileu, leu could be present in each protein. Basic amino acids are absent.

The remarkable similarity in the molar ratios of the amino acids offers encouragement to the proposition that common peptides will be found in the electrophoretic components of the serum proteins. The peptide of spot 7 probably differs from spot 8 in leucine content, which would account for the higher R_f of spot 8. More encouraging are the recent reports of Edelman (2, 13) who found that gamma-globulin, the Bence-Jones proteins, and the myeloma proteins have a peptide unit of common amino acid composition.

Such a system was predicted from our calculations (Table V), and from the comparison of the partial acid hydrolyzates early as 1958 (35). Thus from Equation 1 (see Table III) the values of $n/K \times 100$ yielded Equation 2.

$$-\mu \times 10^5 = 7.7\ K_m - 8.2 \tag{2}$$

The significance of this equation lies in the fact that there must be some intimate relation between the abnormal globulins and the serum proteins, as if part of the serum protein peptides find their way into the globulins, although this may not take place at the same site—that is, it may be a related system.

Both the gamma-globulin system and the serum protein system may be looked upon as a group of template products that represent un-

Table IV. Amino Acid Analysis of Eluates of Spots 7 and 8

Amino Acid	Protein				
	Albumin	Globulins			
		α-1	α-2	β	γ

Peptide 7

Thr	0.7	0.5	0.6	0.7	0.6
Ser	1.0	1.0	1.0	1.0	1.0
Glu	0.8	1.0	0.8	0.9	0.6
Gly	1.2	1.2	1.2	1.0	0.7
Ala	1.0	0.7	0.8	0.9	0.7
Val	1.5	1.3	1.5	1.3	1.0
Ileu	0.4	0.7	0.6	0.4	0.2
Leu	1.2	1.0	1.0	0.8	0.5

Peptide 8

		β-2			
Thr	1.0	0.5		0.8	0.8
Ser	1.0	1.0		1.0	1.0
Glu	1.0	1.1		1.4	1.2
Pro	0.5			0.9	0.5
Gly	1.1	1.2		1.2	1.0
Ala	1.0	0.7		1.0	0.8
Val	1.2	0.6		1.3	1.0
Ileu	0.9	0.6		0.9	0.8
Leu	2.0	1.3		2.3	1.4
Phe	0.7	0.1		0.8	0.6

Table V. Absolute μ and n/K Values of four Myeloma Proteins (40)

Protein	(n/K) 100 [a]	K_m [b]	$-\mu \times 10^5$	
			Calcd.	Obsd.
A	13.4	1.128	0.5	0.5
B	15.5	1.192	1.0	1.0
C	22.0	1.345	2.2	2.1
D	34.0	1.534	3.6	3.6

[a] n/K corrected to unit molecular weight = 160,000.
[b] $K_m = \log (n \times 100/K)$.

differentiated proteins when compared to the highly differentiated highly organized proteins of specific function seen in enzymes. The serum proteins may, therefore, provide a means of examining the products of a template prior to their subsequent refinement into molecules of specific function. This is not so far-fetched, for Sŏrm recently reviewed his highly successful search (44) for common sequences in enzymes, and to achieve this he has developed a "substitution" theory to provide an amino acid or "wild card" to fill an "inside straight" where needed.

Conclusions

In the light of the most recent discoveries referred to above, certain implications may be worthy of mention as to the direction in which future findings can lead. Although evidence accumulating since the early recognition of a number of electrophoretic components and circulatory antibodies suggested that the gamma-globulins were heterogeneous and probably a family of proteins, direct chemical evidence of such interrelationship between specific molecular species was not demonstrated.

Porter's concept of the "structure" of gamma-globulins (32) must not be confused with the actual primary structure. Thus, if there are four chains, two light and two heavy, in every "gamma-globulin," their differences lie in the composition of the chains (11). Edelman has shown that the myeloma globulin and the 7s gamma-globulin have L chains in common; and that the Bence-Jones protein is the L chain. This again is in terms of chemical composition and physical properties, not primary structure. However, data on the heterogeneity of Bence-Jones proteins (14) would indicate that the L chains of the gamma-globulins are heterogeneous.

So what is a gamma-globulin molecule? Could it not be a continuous system of molecular species, each slightly different from the next, wherein their properties would have a gaussian distribution? The concept developed in this report shows how one could examine the properties of a system of closely related proteins in such a way that the molar ratio of certain amino acids, when related to mobility, exclude molecule species that do not belong to the same system. These parameters not only relate one molecular species to another, but possibly suggest their biosynthetic origin.

Literature Cited

(1) Anfinsen, C. B., "Basic Problems in Neoplastic Disease," p. 112, Columbia University Press, New York, 1962.
(2) Berrgard, I., Edelman, G. M., Proc. Natl. Acad. Sci. 49, 330 (1963).
(3) Block, R. J., Ann. N. Y. Acad. Sci. 94, 31 (1961).
(4) Block R. J., J. Biol. Chem. 103, 261 (1933).
(5) Ibid., 105, 455, 461 (1934).
(6) Block, R. J., Durrum, E. L., Zweig, G., "Paper Chromatography and Paper Electrophoresis," Academic Press, New York, 1958.
(7) Block, R. J., in Schmidt, C. L. A., "Chemistry of Amino Acids and Proteins," p. 312., Thomas, Baltimore, Md., 1938.
(8) Block, R. J., Yale J. Biol Med. 7, 235 (1935).
(9) Brand, E., Ann. N. Y. Acad. Sci. 47, 187 (1946).
(10) Brand, E., Edsall, J. T., Ann. Rev. Biol. Chem. 16, 233 (1947).
(11) Cohen, S., Biochem. J. 88, 2P (1963).
(12) Crampton, C. F., Stein, W. H., Moore, S., J. Biol. Chem. 225, 363 (1957).
(13) Edelman, G. M., Galley, J. A., J. Exptl. Med. 116, 207 (1962).

(14) Fried, M., Putnam, F. M., J. Biol. Chem. 235, 3472 (1960).
(15) Hardy, W. B., J. Physiol. 33, 251 (1905).
(16) Henning, U., Helinski, D. R., Chao, F. C., Yanofsky, C., J. Biol. Chem. 237, 1523 (1962).
(17) Hill, R. J., Konigsberg, W., Guidotti, G., Craig, L. C., Ibid., 237, 1549 (1962).
(18) Hirs, C. W. H., Moore, S., Stein, W. H., Ibid., 235, 633 (1960).
(19) Kassel, B., Laskowski, M., Sr., Ibid., 236, 1996 (1961).
(20) Koshland, D. E., Advan. Enzymol. 22, 45 (1960).
(21) Kossel, A., Z. Physiol. Chem. 44 347 (1905).
(22) Long, C., "Biochemists' Handbook," p. 765, Van Nostrand, Princeton, N. J., 1961.
(23) Manowald, T. A., Noltmann, E. A., Kuby, S. A., J. Biol. Chem. 237, 1138 (1962).
(24) Margoliash, E., Smith, E. L., Ibid., 237, 2151 (1962).
(25) Millar, D. B. S., Ibid., 237, 2135 (1962).
(26) Miller, L. L., Bly, C. G., Watson, M. L., Bale, W. F., J. Exptl. Med. 94, 431 (1951).
(27) Neurath, H., Proc. 3rd Intern. Congr. Biochem., Brussels, 1955, p. 89, 1956.
(28) Nirenberg, M. W., Matthaei, J. H., Jones, O. W., Martin, R. G., Barondes, S. H., Federation Proc. 22, 55 (1963).
(29) Noltmann, E. A., Manowald, T. A., Kuby, S. A., J. Biol. Chem. 237, 1146 (1962).
(30) Peters T., Jr., Ibid., 237, 2182 (1962).
(31) Porter, R. R., "Basic Problems in Neoplastic Disease," p. 177, Columbia University Press, New York, 1962.
(32) Putnam, F. W., ed., "The Plasma Proteins," Academic Press, New York, 1960.
(33) Schultz, J., J. Polymer Sci. 49, 25 (1961).
(34) Schultz, J., Allison, H., Grice, M., Biochemistry 1, 694 (1962).
(35) Schultz, J., Delavan, L., Abstracts, 134th Meeting ACS, p. 60C, 1958.
(36) Schultz, J., Grannis, G., Kimmel, H., Shay, H., Federation Proc. 14, 134 (1955).
(37) Schultz, J., Grannis, G., Kimmel, H., Shay, H., Arch. Biochem. Biophys. 57, 174 (1955).
(38) Schultz, J., Jamison, W., Shay, H., Greenstein, M., Ibid., 50, 124 (1954).
(39) Smith, E. L., Brown, D. M., McFadden, M. L., Buettner-Janusch, V., Jager, B. V., J. Biol. Chem. 216, 601 (1955).
(40) Smith, E. L., Stockwell, A., Ibid., 207, 501 (1954).
(41) Smithies, O., Biochem. J. 61, 629 (1955).
(42) Sober, H. A., Gutter, F. J., Wyckoff, M. M., Peterson, E. A., J. Am. Chem. Soc. 78, 756 (1956).
(43) Sorensen, S. P. L., Compt. Rend. Trav. Lab. Carlsberg 18 (5), 1 (1930).
(44) Sörm, F., Advan. Enzymol 24, 415 (1962).
(45) Tristram, G. R., in "The Proteins," Vol. I, Part A, Academic Press, New York, 1953.

Received May 14, 1963. Work supported in part by the National Institutes of Health, U. S. Public Health Service Grant C-3715, and the Damon Runyon Fund Grant DRG-473.

2

Dominant Role of the Liver in Biosynthesis of the Plasma Proteins with Special Reference to the Plasma Mucoproteins (Seromucoid), Ceruloplasmin, and Fibrinogen

LEON L. MILLER, HELEN R. HANAVAN, NANTHA TITTHASIRI, AND ANUBHA CHOWDHURY

Department of Radiation Biology, School of Medicine and Dentistry, University of Rochester, Rochester, N. Y.

The techniques of isolated rat liver perfusion, preparative starch-block electrophoresis, and the use of isotopically labeled metabolites (lysine-6-C^{14}, leucine-1-C^{14}, sulfur^{35}-labeled sulfate, and copper^{64}) have been combined to examine more critically previously published conclusions that the liver is the site of biosynthesis of plasma albumin, and of the plasma α-globulins and β-globulins, including fibrinogen. The data reaffirm the view that all plasma albumin, virtually all of the normally occurring perchloric acid nonprecipitable proteins (seromucoid), ceruloplasmin, the plasma lipoproteins, and all fibrinogen are synthesized by the liver. Data support the view that nonhepatic tissues are primarily concerned with producing γ-globulins and β-globulins generically related to the γ-globulins. Also described are net biosynthesis of fibrinogen and its inhibition by puromycin, mitomycin, and ethionine in the isolated perfused liver.

More than ten years ago we devised a direct approach toward a definition of the role of the liver in plasma protein biosynthesis by combining the techniques of isolated rat liver perfusion, starch-block electrophoresis, and the use of carbon-14–labeled amino acids (**23, 24**). The classical procedure of liver perfusion was greatly simplified and adapted to a study of the small mammalian liver of the rat (25). It was demonstrated that the isolated rat liver perfused with homologous heparinized rat blood simulates physiologically the qualitative and quantitative performance of the liver in the intact rat for 6 to 8 hours. It was quickly recognized that this time interval was more than sufficient to permit detailed observations of the metabolism of isotopically labeled amino acids used, such as lysine and histidine, and to observe their incorporation into the proteins discharged by the liver into the circulating plasma. With the application of preparative zone electrophoresis to the separation of the plasma proteins labeled with C^{14}-amino acids in the course of liver perfusion, it was revealed that the isolated perfused liver incorporated labeled amino acids into all of the plasma protein fractions, with one notable exception, the γ-globulins.

This report describes further studies with the isolated perfused liver, from which it will be clear that the plasma seromucoid—i.e., proteins soluble in 0.64N perchloric acid (34, 35)—plasma fibrinogen, and ceruloplasmin are synthesized exclusively by the liver.

In the case of fibrinogen by utilizing defibrinated rat blood for liver perfusion, it has been possible to demonstrate impressive net biosynthesis of fibrinogen protein to an extent depending upon the degree of hypofibrinogenemia in the circulating perfusing blood.

By way of supplementing and controlling the observations made with isolated liver perfusion, studies have been carried out on the eviscerated surviving rat (all abdominal viscera excepting kidneys removed) and the hepatectomized rat, and their plasmas subjected to similar fractionation techniques. In a number of experiments the eviscerated surviving rat was prepared in such a manner as to leave the liver hepatic arterial circulation intact. Such a rat had all abdominal viscera except the kidneys and liver excised. In keeping with the conclusions derivable from the liver perfusion studies, the studies in the eviscerated surviving rat and the hepatectomized rat demonstrate that the nonhepatic tissues are primarily concerned with the biosynthesis of the γ-globulins and some β-globulins which may be related to the γ-globulins.

Methods and Experimental

Adult male Sprague-Dawley rats weighing 250 to 450 grams were used in most of these studies. They were maintained on commercial rat food and were allowed access to water at all times.

The techniques of isolated liver perfusion and the preparation of eviscerated surviving rat have been described in detail (24, 25). The eviscerated surviving rat was prepared according to the procedure of Ingle (13); the totally hepatectomized rat was prepared according to the two-stage procedure of Meehan (21). DL-lysine-6-C^{14}·HCl and acetate-1-C^{14} were prepared in this laboratory by accepted methods and were chromatographically and radiochemically homogeneous. Carrier-free sulfur-35–labeled sulfate was obtained from the Oak Ridge National Laboratories and used without further purification. Cu^{64} acetate was obtained as a sterile solution from Abbott Laboratories. The manufacturer's assay of the $S^{35}O_4$ and Cu^{64} acetate was used in dilutions of the dose. In all cases the radioactive dose was introduced into the perfusion or injected intravenously in small volumes (1 to 4 ml.) of Ringer's solution. In the ceruloplasmin study Cu^{64} acetate was found very toxic if given intravenously; it was therefore injected intramuscularly in the eviscerated surviving rat.

In liver perfusions samples of blood were generally removed at hourly intervals after a zero time sample at the outset. Samples of blood obtained from the perfusions or at the termination (5 to 6 hours) of eviscerated surviving rat or hepatectomized rat experiments were centrifuged and the plasma was harvested and mixed with 1 ml. of 0.9% sodium chloride solution containing carrier lysine, carrier acetate, or carrier sulfate. The plasmas were then dialyzed at 4° C. against three or four changes of physiological saline, the latter being changed at least three times in the course of 24 hours.

At the close of the dialysis the plasma was centrifuged to remove small amounts of precipitate and the clear plasma resulting was subjected to starch-block preparative zone electrophoresis by the technique of Kunkel and Slater (15). At the close of the electrophoresis 1-cm. segments of the starch block were cut and transferred to sintered glass funnels, and the proteins were quantitatively eluted with five successive 2-ml. aliquots of 0.9% sodium chloride. The filtrates containing the protein fractions were then made up to a constant volume and mixed, and small aliquots were analyzed for total protein content by the method of Lowry et al. (18).

To each tube a sufficient quantity of concentrated perchloric acid (12.1N) was added with a serological pipet to give a final concentration of 0.64N perchloric acid. The tubes were mixed rapidly after the addition of perchloric acid, allowed to stand at room temperature for 10 minutes, and centrifuged rapidly for 10 minutes at 3000 r.p.m. in a Type 3 International centrifuge. The clear or slightly opalescent supernatant fluid was quantitatively transferred to a corresponding series of tubes and aliquots were again removed for protein analysis. Proteins soluble in 0.64 M perchloric were arbitrarily designated seromucoids. The seromucoids were quantitatively precipitated by the further addition of 5% phosphotungstate in 2N HCl and the resultant precipitates were centrifuged off. Precipitates were then quantitatively transferred to combustion flasks and converted to carbon dioxide with the digestion mixture of Van Slyke, Plazin, and Weisiger (33), and their C^{14} content was determined in an ionization chamber with the vibrating reed electrometer. Results of all C^{14} assays are arbitrarily expressed in terms of volts per minute, where 1 volt per minute is equivalent to 2.1×10^4 disintegrations per minute.

In experiments in which sulfur-35–labeled sulfate was used, the supernatant solutions containing the plasma seromucoids were mixed with 1.0 ml. of 1% sodium sulfate and digested on a steam bath with 10 ml. of 20% HCl for about 2 hours, a time sufficient to convert all ester sulfate to inorganic sulfate. After an excess of 5% barium chloride was added, precipitates were digested for another 20 or 30 minutes on a steam bath and centrifuged. Supernatant clear fluid was removed, and the precipitates were washed once with dilute HCl, then with 95% ethyl alcohol, and transferred quantitatively to planchette cups as a slurry with the aid of small volumes of alcohol. The alcohol was allowed to evaporate, leaving a uniform deposit of barium sulfate which was assayed for radioactivity in a windowless flow counter. The amount of carrier sulfate added was such that the precipitates were assayed essentially at infinite thickness.

In a number of experiments studying the incorporation of $S^{35}O_4$ into seromucoid fractions 10-μl. samples of plasma were applied to paper strips and subjected to electrophoresis in the Beckman-Spinco paper electrophoresis apparatus. The resultant oven-dried paper strips were attached to an 8×10 sheet of paper and applied directly to a sheet of Eastman No-screen x-ray film. Exposure extended over a period of 1 month. At the end of this time the film was developed in the usual manner (see Figure 2). The paper strips were then stained with bromophenol blue to demonstrate the major protein fractions.

In the ceruloplasmin experiments appropriate aliquots of specimens were placed in small test tubes and assayed for Cu^{64} activity in a well-type scintillation counter. Analyses were made with reference to a Cu^{64} standard prepared and assayed at the outset and whenever other samples were assayed. This permitted correction for radioactivity decay of this 12.8-hour half-life isotope.

Experimental Results

Figure 1 presents results of the electrophoretic separation of plasma proteins from an isolated perfused rat liver experiment to which both DL-lysine-6-C^{14} and $S^{35}O_4$ were added. It is clear that the seromucoid fractions are primarily restricted to the albumin, α-, and β-globulin regions, and correspond to the MP_1 and MP_2 fractions of Mehl, Humphrey, and Winzler (22). The quantitative variations in the incorporation of C^{14} and $S^{35}O_4$ are best interpreted in terms of the seromucoid fractions being grossly heterogeneous. All of the plasma seromucoid fractions contained significant amounts of carbon-14 and sulfur-35 sulfate. The amounts of lysine-C^{14} present are roughly proportional to the amounts of protein in the seromucoid fractions. The largest amount of sulfate-35 activity is associated with the fast-moving leading edge of the seromucoid fraction.

Figure 2 presents the results of autoradiography of the electrophoretically separated plasma protein fractions taken at zero time and at hourly intervals during the course of an isolated liver perfusion to which only sulfur-35-labeled sulfate had been added. The zero time control strip reveals no significant activity associated with any of the plasma protein fractions. Radioactivity of the protein fractions is seen as early as 1 hour and appears with increasing intensity in a variety of fractions comparable with seromucoid fractions noted in the starch-block electrophoresis. Of some interest is the appearance of two radioactive fractions moving well ahead of the albumin. Their identity remains to be established. In Figure 2 the arabic numbers refer only to

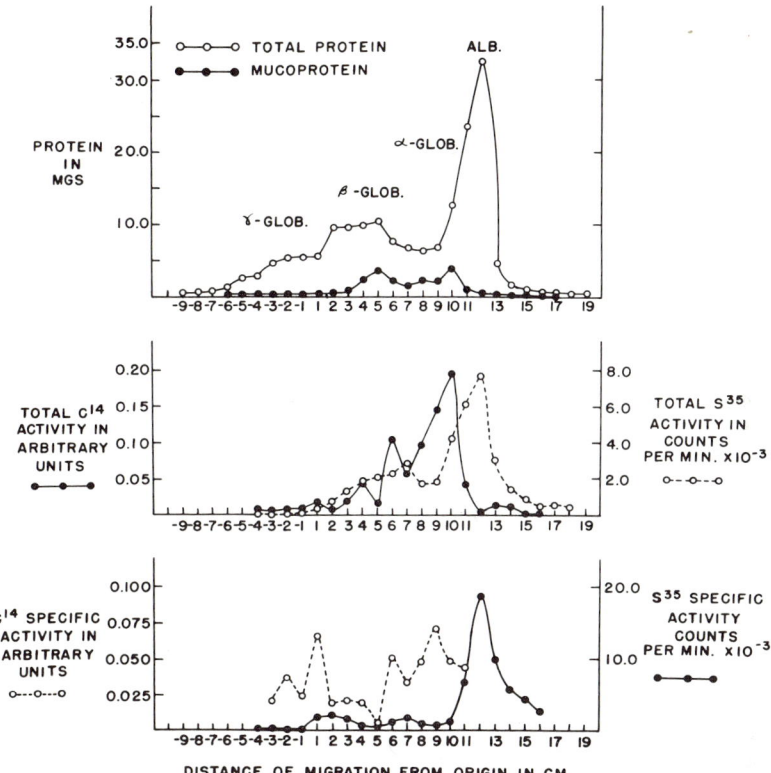

Figure 1. Electrophoretic separation of plasma mucoproteins from isolated perfused rat liver with $S^{35}O_4^{-2}$ and lysine-6-C^{14}

Liver and blood donors, 18 hours fasted. Liver weight, 6.25 grams. Perfusion blood volume, 181 ml. containing 500 mg. glucose. 1000 mg. glucose total infused continuously in 17.5 ml. Ringer's solution through 6 hours' perfusion. Dose, 12.0 mg. DL-lysine-6-C^{14} · HCl (600 volts/min. as L-lysine-6-C^{14}). $S^{35}O_4$ as carrier-free sulfate (total activity, 400 microcuries). 4.0 ml. dialyzed plasma (total C^{14} activity, 1.752 volts/min.) separated by electrophoresis. After electrophoresis, total C^{14} in nonmucoprotein fractions was 0.928 volt/min.; in mucoprotein fractions, 0.812 volt/min.

the gross order of intensity of the various autoradiographically detectable fractions.

Figure 3 shows the results of the electrophoretic separation of a specimen of plasma taken from an eviscerated surviving rat 4 hours after an infusion of 320 microcuries of $S^{35}O_4$ given as carrier-free inorganic sulfate and analogous to the dose used in the isolated liver perfusion of Figure 1. The lower half of Figure 3 reveals that the amounts of S^{35} present in the seromucoid fractions of the plasma from the evis-

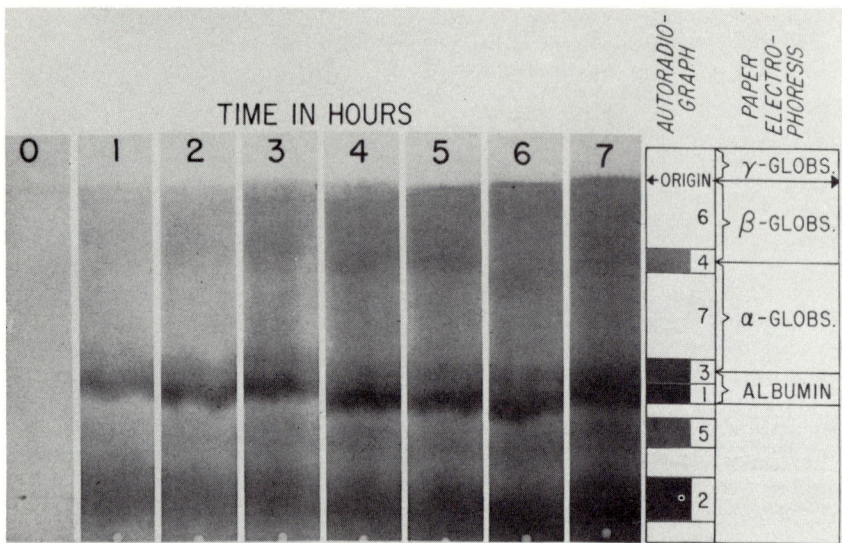

Figure 2. Autoradiograph of plasma proteins labeled with $S^{35}O_4$ by isolated perfused rat liver

Blood and liver donors not fasted. Liver donor weight, 396 grams. Liver weight, 11.6 grams. Perfusion blood volume, 106 ml. Dose of 6.0 millicuries carrier-free $S^{35}O_4$ mixed into perfusion blood at zero time. Samples of blood, 2.2 to 3.5 ml. taken hourly, experiment terminated at 7 hours. Perfusion rate, 13 to 15 ml./min. throughout. Total bile volume, 2.9 ml. Samples of plasma, 10μl. each, placed on paper strips and electrophoresed with Veronal buffer, ionic strength, 0.5, pH 8.5. Strips oven-dried 10 min. at 105° before 1-month exposure to No-screen x-ray film (Eastman Kodak Co.). Strips stained with bromophenol blue according to Beckman-Spinco manual. Location of stained protein fractions shown by brackets in diagram on right

cerated rat are detectable but unimpressively small and only a tiny fraction of the activity incorporated into the plasma seromucoid by the isolated rat liver. The curve for the latter comparison is the same as that in Figure 1.

If this comparison is to be meaningful, it is necessary to assume that the specific activities of precursor sulfate in the isolated rat liver perfusion and in the eviscerated surviving rat were essentially similar. Although specific activities of the sulfate were not actually measured, it seems reasonable to assume that, if anything, the specific activity of the sulfate in the liver perfusion was lower than that in the eviscerated surviving rat. The blood volume in the former is roughly five to six times the intra- and extravascular fluid volume of the eviscerated rat. The failure to incorporate significant amounts of sulfate into the plasma seromucoid by the eviscerated surviving rat is not surprising, in view of the fact that lysine-C^{14} was not incorporated into the plasma sero-

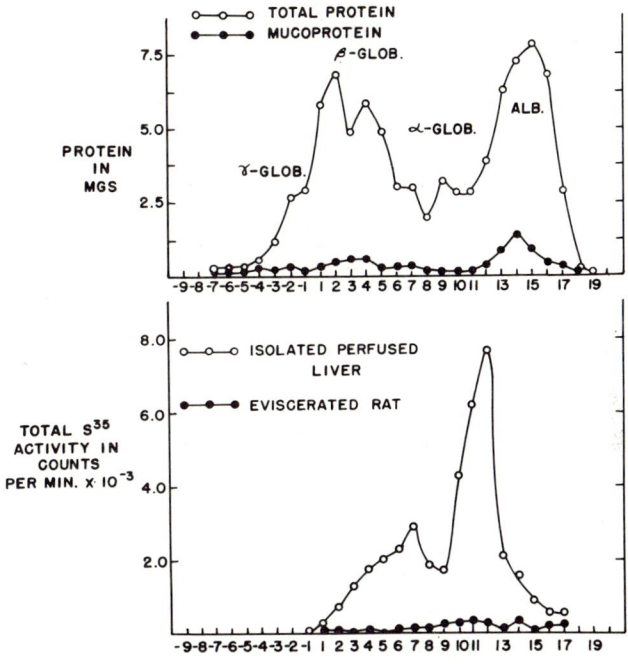

Figure 3. Electrophoretic separation of plasma mucoproteins from surviving eviscerated rat with $S^{35}O_4^{-2}$ (upper) and comparison of $S^{35}O_4$ incorporation by eviscerated rat and isolated liver (lower)

Rat wt., 400 grams. After total evisceration, dose 320 microcuries carrier-free $S^{35}O_4$ given intravenously at zero time. Continuous infusion 10% glucose in Ringer's solution; 1.35 ml. plus 0.16 unit insulin per hour for 4 hours of experiment. 2 ml. dialyzed plasma separated by electrophoresis and resulting fractions treated with perchloric acid to obtain mucoproteins. Measured $S^{35}O_4$ activity of eviscerated rat plasma mucoprotein fractions multiplied by 2 X 1.5 to permit indicated comparison with data from 4 ml. of plasma of 6-hour experiment of isolated rat liver perfusion of Figure 1

mucoid fractions of the eviscerated surviving rat or the hepatectomized rat.

Figure 4 presents the results of electrophoretic separation of plasma protein fractions obtained after perfusion of an isolated rat liver with acetate-1-C^{14}. For the purposes of this presentation, it is noteworthy that virtually all of the activity associated with plasma protein fractions 8 through 13 was present in the seromucoid fractions and

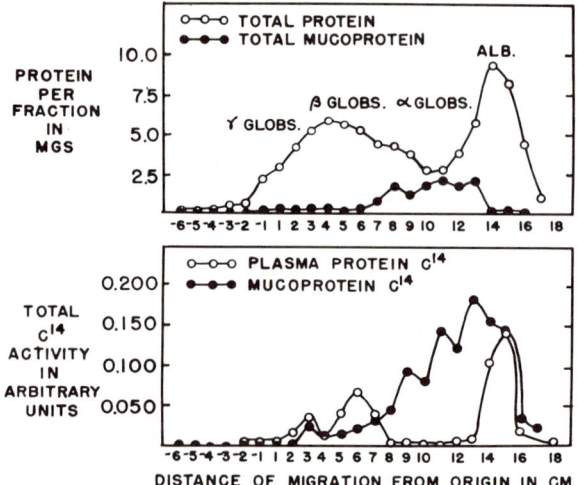

Figure 4. Electrophoretic separation of plasma protein from isolated rat liver perfusion with acetate-1-C^{14}

Liver donor fed, blood donors fasted. Liver weight, 10.2 grams. Perfusion blood volume, 202 ml. Solution of 35 mg. sodium acetate-1-C^{14} plus 500 mg. glucose in 16 ml. of Ringer's solution given by continuous infusion for first 2 1/2 hours of 6-hour perfusion. Six-hour sample of dialyzed plasma, 4.0 ml. separated by electrophoresis

that the highest C^{14}-activity derivable from acetate in the seromucoids is seen in the leading edge of the seromucoid fractions, mainly 13, 14, and 15. It is this portion of the seromucoid fractions which we previously noted in Figure 1 had the highest specific sulfate activity.

A significant portion of the seromucoid radioactivity was presumably associated with plasma lipids.

After the seromucoids were precipitated with phosphotungstate-HCl, they were exhaustively extracted with hot alcohol-ether (3 to 1 by volume), followed by two hot extractions with chloroform-methanol (1 to 1). The combined solvent extracts were evaporated on the steam bath under nitrogen and the lipids taken up with petroleum ether. The petroleum ether extracts were washed several times with water containing acetate and β-hydroxybutyrate and acetoacetate (10).

The combined washed petroleum ether extracts of the seromucoid fractions contained 41% of the total seromucoid-C^{14}-activity; the combined petroleum ether extracts of the nonseromucoid protein fractions contained 37% of the total C^{14}-activity present in those fractions before extraction. Such an experiment with acetate-1-C^{14} leaves open questions concerning the nature of the nonlipide activity. On the basis of known metabolic conversions of acetate-1-C^{14}, glutamic and aspartic acids as well as glucose, mannose, and hexosamines could conceivably be labeled.

Because the plasma seromucoids appear in increased concentrations in the blood of animals with inflammatory processes or malignant tumors (34), we studied the patterns of C^{14}-incorporation into the plasma proteins of a number of rats bearing subcutaneously implanted Walker carcinoma 256.

Figure 5 presents the results of electrophoretic fractionation of plasma proteins obtained from an eviscerated surviving tumor-bearing

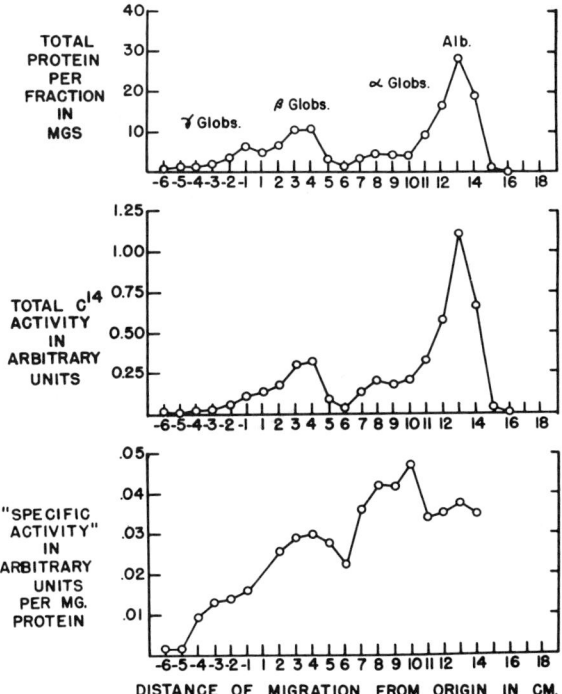

Figure 5. Electrophoretic separation of C^{14}-labeled proteins from eviscerated surviving rat (with liver)

Walker tumor present

Rat wt., 470 grams. Eviscerated by usual procedure, except liver left with functioning hepatic arterial blood supply. Tumor wt., 37 grams; dose given at zero time, 6.0 mg. DL-lysine-6-C^{14} · HCl (340 volts/min. as L-lysine-6-C^{14}). Experiment terminated at 6 hours. 2.0 ml. dialyzed plasma (total C^{14} activity 3.152 volts/min.) separated by electrophoresis

rat in which the liver was left functionally intact supplied with the hepatic artery. Here the liver is supplied with blood in spite of the absence of the gastrointestinal tract, spleen, pancreas, and other mesenteric structures. Figure 5 reveals that in spite of the absence of these nonhepatic viscera, the pattern of C^{14}-incorporation into the plasma proteins is not qualitatively different from that noted in the normal non-tumor-bearing, unoperated rat [for comparison see (23)]. Here it is obvious that the α-globulins, which we know include many of the seromucoids, have the highest specific activity, followed by the albumin, the β-globulin, and the γ-globulin fractions. This is roughly the order of incorporation previously noted in the normal animal and in the isolated perfused liver (23, 24).

Figure 6 presents the results of a parallel study in which the eviscerated surviving tumor-bearing rat was also surgically deprived of its liver. There are a number of striking quantitative and qualitative differences between the pattern of incorporation noted in this animal without a liver and that found in the experiment of Figure 5 in which the eviscerated rat retained its liver. Qualitatively one notes in Figure 6 the dominant incorporation into the γ-globulins with highest specific activity, and into the β-globulins. Similarly to the pattern we have described, for the normal eviscerated surviving rat, there are here small quantitatively insignificant amounts of radioactivity in the α-globulin and albumin fractions.

It is important to recognize that with a given dose of lysine-C^{14}, the total C^{14} activity incorporated into the plasma proteins of the eviscerated surviving rat without a liver in this and similar experiments is about 10% of the total activity incorporated into the plasma proteins by an intact animal, or by an eviscerated surviving rat with the liver left functionally intact supplied with the hepatic artery, or by the isolated perfused liver. This comparison is quantitatively the more impressive if one recalls that in the presence of the normally functioning liver a major fraction (15 to 50% of an L-lysine-C^{14} dose) is oxidized to carbon dioxide (26). In the absence of the liver, oxidation of labeled lysine to $C^{14}O_2$ is approximately 1/20 that seen in the presence of the liver (23, 24, 25). When the seromucoid fractions (those proteins soluble in 0.64N perchloric acid and insoluble in phosphotungstate HCl) from the totally eviscerated rat experiments—e.g., that of Figure 6—were assayed for C^{14}, they contained no significant activity. Such results add to the evidence indicating that the nonhepatic tissues do not produce plasma seromucoids, even in rats harboring an experimental tumor presumably known to enhance the synthesis of plasma seromucoids.

Figure 7 presents the results of a study in which a totally hepatectomized rat maintained alive with a continuous infusion of glucose and Ringer's solution was given lysine-6-C^{14} intravenously. Although the separate individual small fractions from the electrophoresis were not assayed individually, they were pooled according to the grossly perceptible electrophoretic pattern as determined by analysis of protein and indicated by the dotted lines. Appropriate aliquots of these fraction pools were analyzed for C^{14} and the results are indicated in the table associated with Figure 7. Here again it is apparent that there are

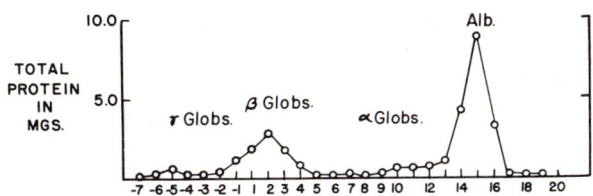
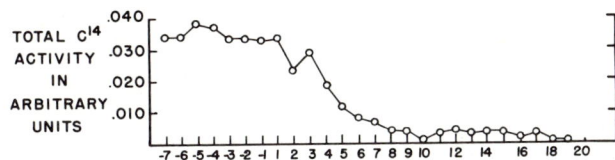
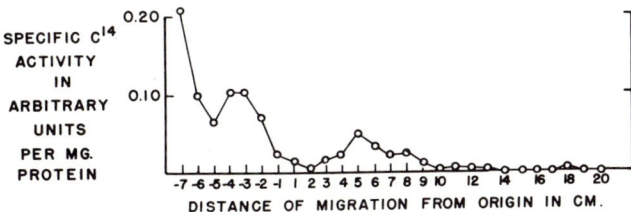

Figure 6. Electrophoretic separation of plasma protein fractions of plasma from eviscerated surviving tumor-bearing rat injected with DL-lysine-ϵ-C^{14} · HCl

Rat wt., 345 grams. Tumor wt., 33.8 grams. Dose given at zero time, 6.76 mg. DL-lysine-6-C^{14} · HCl (383 volts/min. as L-lysine-6-C^{14}); 10% glucose in Ringer's solution 1.35 ml. plus 0.16 unit crystalline zinc insulin per hour by continuous intravenous infusion. Experiment terminated at 6 hours. 1.75 ml. heparinized dialyzed plasma (total C^{14} activity, 0.49 volt/min.) separated by electrophoresis

measurable but small amounts of radioactivity associated with the albumin and α-globulin fractions and that the major C^{14}-activity is associated with the γ- and β-globulin fractions. A line of separation of γ- from β-globulins in this, as in most preparative electrophoretic patterns, is not clearly demarkable. Hence, the exact distinction between the γ and β fractions is arbitrary.

What is to be emphasized here is the fact that the per cent dose incorporation into the γ- plus β-globulin fractions of the plasma proteins of the hepatectomized rat is not measurably different from that noted in the eviscerated surviving rat. In other words, the concomitant presence of the gastrointestinal tract, pancreas, spleen, and mesentery structures has not grossly altered the qualitative or quantitative pat-

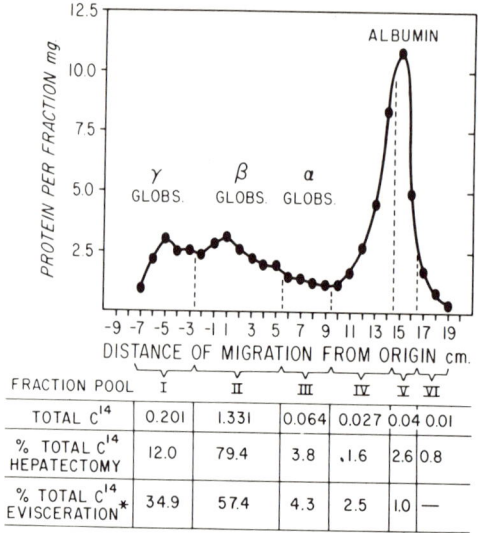

Figure 7. Electrophoretic separation of plasma proteins from hepatectomized rat given DL-lysine-6-C^{14}

Rat wt., 204 grams. Dose, 1.24 mg. DL-lysine-6-C^{14} · HCl (1100 volts/min. as L-lysine-6-C^{14}). Continuous intravenous infusion of 10% glucose in Ringer's solution; total, 7.4 ml. Experiment terminated at 6 hours. 2.0 ml. heparinized dialyzed plasma (total activity, 1.68 volts/min.) separated by electrophoresis

*Calculated from (24)

terns of lysine-C^{14} incorporation into the plasma proteins. A large aliquot volume of each of the fraction pools was precipitated with perchloric acid (final concentration, 0.64N) and the residual mucoproteins were precipitated with phosphotungstate-HCl. The seromucoid fractions so obtained were essentially without radioactivity, indicating that the hepatectomized rat does not incorporate significant lysine-C^{14} into the plasma seromucoid fractions.

Evidence for Ceruloplasmin Synthesis from Cu^{64} by Isolated Liver. Figure 8 shows the linear disappearance of Cu^{64} activity from the perfusion blood during the first 4 hours of a 5-hour perfusion. Analyses of small lobes of the liver removed at 5 minutes, 3 hours, and 5 hours revealed that at least 53% of the initial Cu^{64} activity was retained by the liver and more than 10% was in the bile collected during the perfusion. Preferential concentration of parenterally administered Cu^{64} in the liver of intact animals has been described (16).

As seen in Figure 9, the residual blood Cu^{64} activity was largely associated with the albumin and with those electrophoretic fractions having mobilities of α_2-β-globulins. The marked percentage increase in the latter, seen as early as 2 hours and marked at 5 hours, was in striking contrast to the distribution at zero time. In this connection of

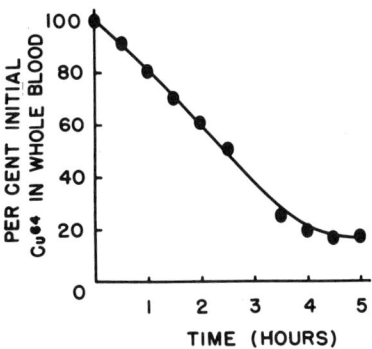

Figure 8. Per cent of initial Cu^{64} activity remaining in circulating blood during isolated perfusion of rat liver

Perfusion blood volume, 83 ml.; liver weight, 11.9 grams, from fed donors. Added to blood at outset, 327 mg. of mixture of essential and nonessential amino acids (25) and 150 mg. glucose plus 1.25 millicuries (7.0 × 10^7 counts per min. 0.8 mg. Cu as cupric acetate). Small lobes of liver removed at 5 min., 3 hours, and 5 hours. Analysis of homogenates of these specimens for Cu^{64} activity showed 4.5, 38.8, 53.0% of activity estimated present in liver at 5 min., 3 hours, and 5 hours, respectively. By close of experiment 2.2 ml. of bile had been secreted. Bile contained 10.8% of initial total Cu^{64} activity. Residual blood contained 18%

interest is the electrophoretic Cu^{64} distribution in the plasma obtained 4-1/2 hours after an identical dose of Cu^{64} acetate was given intramuscularly to an eviscerated surviving rat. Here, the pattern of Cu^{64} distribution was indistinguishable from the zero-hour plasma of the isolated liver perfusion. Only the albumin fraction of the eviscerated rat plasma was associated with high Cu^{64} activity—77% of the total in the

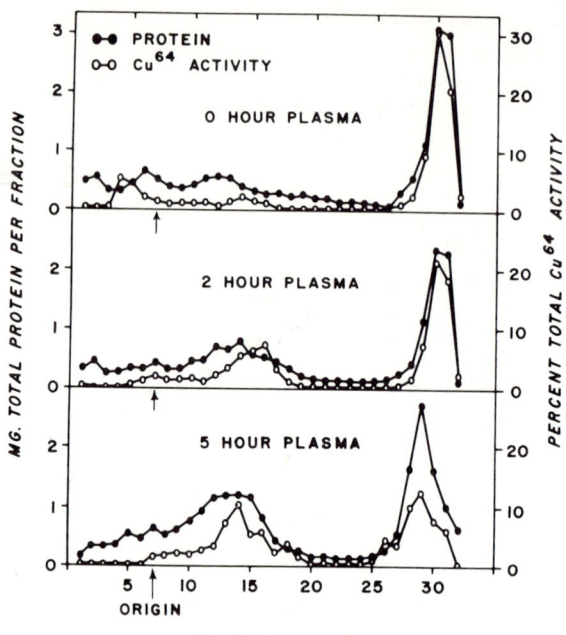

Figure 9. Results of simultaneous preparative electrophoresis of equal samples (0.5 ml.) of plasma obtained from blood taken 0, 2, and 5 hours after start of liver perfusion (Figure 8)

Plasmas not dialyzed before electrophoresis. For each fraction, results expressed in terms of percentage of total Cu^{64} activity associated with all fractions at end of electrophoresis. (Actual total Cu^{64} activity of all fractions 0 hr., 1.78×10^5 counts/min.; 2 hr., 7.18×10^4 counts/min.; 5 hr., 1.36×10^4 counts/min.) In comparable study, 388-gram eviscerated surviving rat given 1.25 Mc. of Cu^{64} acetate intramuscularly. After 4 1/2 hours 1.0 ml. blood contained 1.0×10^5 counts/min. Electrophoretic separation of plasma showed 77% of Cu^{64} associated with albumin fractions, 1 to 3% in each α-globulin fraction (total 10%), 1 to 3% in each β-globulin fraction (total 10%), and about 3% in γ-globulins

plasma. The copper associated with the albumin is loosely bound and exchangeable with ionic copper under physiologic conditions; in contrast, ceruloplasmin copper is firmly bound and nonexchangeable (**31**).

Fibrinogen Biosynthesis by Isolated Liver. In our isolated rat liver perfusion studies homologous heparinized oxygenated rat blood is routinely diluted with Ringer's solution, so that its final volume is increased by one third of the volume of whole blood used. Thus, the initial concentration of blood plasma fibrinogen is somewhat lower than the normal of about 250 mg. %. Figure 10 reveals that in the course of such a perfusion there is a small decrease in the concentration of the circulating fibrinogen during the first 4 hours. Only at the end of the experiment (6 hours) was there a measurable increase in the blood fibrinogen level sufficient, as the data indicate, to account for a production of approximately 0.2 mg. of fibrinogen per gram of liver per hour.

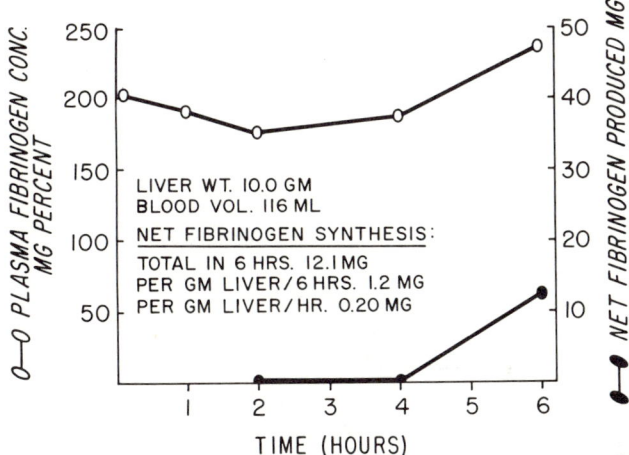

Figure 10. Fibrinogen biosynthesis

Liver and blood donor, 18-hours fasted. Perfusion blood drawn as usual by cardiac puncture with heparin (Upjohn, 1 to 50,000), total volume, 7.0 ml., then shaken with glass beads to simulate defibrination. Blood strained through several layers of surgical gauze. Glucose, 250 mg., added to blood before start of perfusion. Samples taken at zero time, 2, 4, and 6 hours, when experiment was terminated. Plasma samples, 2.0 ml., diluted with 20 ml. 0.9% sodium chloride and mixed rapidly in order with 1.0 ml. of 2.5% calcium chloride, 0.5 ml. of 2.5% protamine sulfate to neutralize heparin, and 0.5 ml. (50 units) of freshly prepared solution of lyophilized bovine thrombin (Parke Davis and Co.). After 2 hours at room temperature fibrin clots were centrifuged, supernatant solution removed, and fibrin washed twice with 0.9% sodium chloride and centrifuged after each washing. Fibrin solubilized with 1.0 ml. of 1N sodium hydroxide and aliquots taken for measurement of protein content by method of Lowry et al. (18)

The results of Figure 11 are in striking contrast. Here, when the liver perfusion is carried out with completely defibrinated blood, there is a remarkable net synthesis of fibrinogen which becomes prominent only after the second to third hour and is impressive by the fifth and sixth hours. The chemically measured circulating level of fibrinogen has increased some 60 mg. % above that present in the zero time specimens. Net synthesis of fibrinogen of this magnitude has been repeatedly obtained in more than 25 perfusion studies which will be detailed elsewhere.

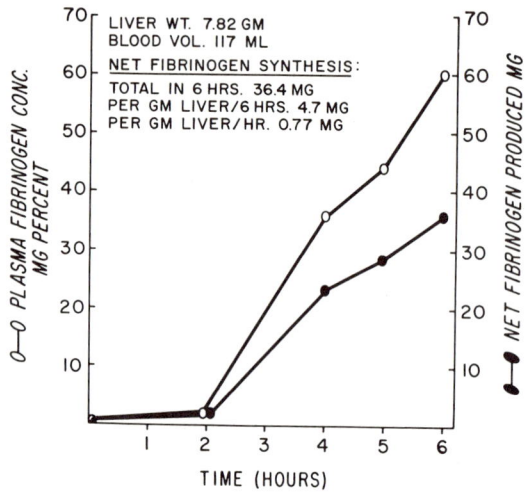

Figure 11. Fibrinogen biosynthesis

Liver and blood donors, 18 hours fasted. Blood drawn by cardiac puncture without anticoagulant and defibrinated by shaking with glass beads. Defibrinated blood strained through several layers of surgical gauze and cells separated from defibrinated plasma by centrifuging at 2000 r.p.m. (International Centrifuge, Type 2) for 25 minutes. Slightly hemolyzed hazy plasma then centrifuged for 30 minutes (10,000 g) in refrigerated Servall. (This removed tiny fibrin clots as a gelatinous button and ensured good perfusion rates throughout 6 hours of experiment.) Red cells were then resuspended in transparent defibrinated plasma to reconstitute blood. A complete amino acid mixture, 325 mg. (25), and 250 mg. glucose added to blood before starting perfusion. Samples at 0, 2, 4, 5, and 6 hours processed to give quantitative precipitation of fibrin (see details under Figure 10)

Assumed: (1) Body Weight: 400 G. Liver Weight: 10 G.

(2) TOTAL FIBRINOGEN POOL = 2 (CIRCULATING FIBRINOGEN POOL)

= 2 (PLASMA VOLUME) (250 MG %)

= 2 (0.04) (BODY WT.) (250)

= 80 MG.

Assume: BIOLOGICAL HALF LIFE: 36 Hours

TURNOVER TIME = 1.44 (36) = 50 HOURS

TURNOVER RATE = 80/50 = 1.6 MG/HOUR

= 0.16 MG/G. LIVER/HOUR

Figure 12. Rate of fibrinogen biosynthesis in normal turnover in rat

Under a variety of conditions it has not to date been possible to stimulate fibrinogen biosynthesis above this maximum value. Figure 12 outlines a calculation from which it is clear that the isolated perfused liver can synthesize fibrinogen at a rate three to four times that necessary to meet the needs of normal fibrinogen turnover, which we have found to occur with a half life of 1.5 days in the rat (30).

It is of some interest to inquire whether one may affect the net synthesis of fibrinogen under conditions of extreme hypofibrinogenemia associated with maximal fibrinogen production. Table I reveals that the amino acid analog L-ethionine, 5.6 mg. at the outset of liver perfusion, followed by continuous infusion of 3 mg. per hour after an initial priming dose, greatly suppresses the biosynthesis of fibrinogen.

Puromycin, 10 mg. at the outset and 15-mg. total given by continuous infusion over the course of 5 hours, virtually completely suppresses biosynthesis of fibrinogen, thus exceeding the inhibition observed with L-ethionine. In another experiment not detailed here, puromycin was introduced after 3 hours of perfusion; although the fibrino-

Table I. Inhibition of Net Fibrinogen Biosynthesis by the Isolated Perfused Liver

Inhibitor	Net Fibrinogen Synthesis Mg./G. Liver/Hr.	% Inhibition
None	0.77	
L-Ethionine	0.14, 0.16	80
Puromycin	0.00	100
Mitomycin C	0.37, 0.35	52

gen level at 4 hours was substantially higher than at 3 hours, there was no significant increase after that time, implying that fibrinogen biosynthesis under way was summarily halted.

The antibiotic mitomycin C, introduced to give a concentration of 10 μg. per ml. in the perfusing blood at the outset, and a continuous infusion of a total of 1 mg. over the course of 4 to 5 hours, was also associated with significant suppression of fibrinogen biosynthesis. The concentrations of mitomycin C used here are at least ten times that which significantly inhibited cellular multiplication in isolated cell cultures. Further studies at lower concentration levels with both puromycin and mitomycin C are indicated.

Discussion

In spite of the early demonstration of the dominant role of the liver in the biosynthesis of all plasma protein fractions except the γ-globulins (23, 24), there has been apparent reluctance to accept these observations as extending to specific proteins or groups of proteins. To be sure, the synthesis of plasma albumin exclusively by the liver has been generally accepted, perhaps because our early observations on the synthesis of the electrophoretically separated albumin fraction by the isolated liver were confirmed by others (8) and also because of numerous in vitro studies utilizing various liver preparations pointing to synthesis of serum albumin. The demonstrated absolute failure of the nonhepatic tissues to incorporate significant quantities of lysine-C^{14} into the serum albumin fraction in the eviscerated surviving rat and in the hepatectomized rat are altogether in keeping with the above observations.

The early studies with the isolated perfused liver and the eviscerated surviving rat pointed to the virtually exclusive synthesis of α-globulins by the liver (23, 24). In spite of the fact that in the rat the serum seromucoid fractions have been described to have mobilities similar to the α-globulins as described by Winzler and others (22, 28), there appears to have been general reluctance to accept the liver as the specific major, if not sole, site of synthesis of the plasma mucoproteins. In a recent authoritative review (34) Winzler states: "Virtually nothing is known of the sites of formation or the physiological significance of the serum glycoproteins." This point of view has been echoed by others (6, 14, 29), who have been influenced by the increased plasma glycoprotein levels noted in various inflammatory states, particularly those involving the connective tissues.

If one accepts the view that the serum seromucoids are soluble in 0.64N perchloric acid as described by Winzler, our studies of the isolated perfused liver utilizing lysine and acetate clearly indicate that the serum seromucoids are virtually exclusively synthesized by the liver. The fact that the seromucoid fractions obtained from eviscerated surviving rats, particularly those bearing an experimental tumor, contain no significant carbon-14 activity after a dose of lysine-C^{14} is in keeping with this view. The detailed data of the electrophoretic separations from our experiments with lysine-C^{14} and sulfur-35–labeled sulfate in the seromucoid fractions are interpretable in terms of these fractions being made up of at least several different chemical individuals. This view is especially strengthened by a consideration of the incorporation of sulfur-35–labeled sulfate into the plasma protein fractions as indicated by the autoradiographic study of Figure 2.

One must conclude that the isolated perfused liver is capable of elaborating at least five different fractions containing radiosulfate. At least two of these appear to have mobilities greater than that of serum albumin. Whether one of these is identical with the so-called pre-albumin cannot be ascertained from these data and must await isolation of rat pre-albumin and its characterization. The conclusions from these experiments are in keeping not only with immunoelectrophoretic studies demonstrating the multiplicity of α-globulins but also with a mass of clinical observations which point to the fact that the plasma glycoproteins, particularly those with mobility of α_2-globulins, are greatly increased in a variety of inflammatory states and that their production, as evidenced by the blood level, is impaired only in advanced liver disease (9).

It is in connection with the β-globulin electrophoretic fraction that it is most difficult to resolve clearly the specific role of the liver. In terms of the per cent dose incorporated into the β-globulins, the contribution of the liver from a given dose of lysine-C^{14} is quantitatively considerably larger than that derived from the contribution of the nonhepatic tissues.

In the last few years the isolated perfused rat liver has been used to demonstrate biosynthesis of the plasma lipoprotein fractions by a number of authors (11, 20, 27). Haft and his collaborators (11) have made a careful detailed study with preparative ultracentrifuge fractionation of the high and low density lipoproteins resulting from hepatic biosynthesis using L-lysine-U-C^{14}. Both low and high density lipoprotein fractions contained lysine-U-C^{14}; their biosynthesis is unquestionably a hepatic function. Although Hartmann (12) has sought to implicate the gastrointestinal tract, particularly the duodenum and jejunum, in the biosynthesis of serum lipoproteins, no detailed demonstration or characterization of such has as yet come to our attention.

Because electrophoresis of serum proteins does not cleanly separate the β- and the γ-globulins, it is not unreasonable to assume that, at least in the case of rat serum proteins, there is considerable overlap. The data from the eviscerated surviving rats, even those bearing subcutaneously implanted tumors, and from hepatectomized rats, leave no doubt that the γ-globulins are produced exclusively by nonhepatic tissues. In a number of species, antibody proteins with mobilities with β-globulins have been described (32). In general, the per cent of the dose of labeled lysine incorporated into the γ-β fraction by the nonhepatic tissues is not substantially increased in the hepatectomized rat as compared to the eviscerated rat. This implies that under the conditions of these experiments the contributions of the γ-globulin–producing tissues such as the lymphoid follicles of the gastrointestinal tract, the spleen, and the mesenteric lymph nodes are qualitatively not different from the γ-globulin–producing tissues of nonvisceral structures.

As a result of our studies, and particularly as a result of studies on the site of γ-globulin synthesis, it may be concluded that γ-globulins are produced by the plasma cells and related lymphoid cells and that under certain unusual conditions where the liver may become massively infiltrated with plasma cells as in the cases described by Bearn (5), such cells may conceivably contribute to γ-globulin production. However, under normal conditions, no significant γ-globulins are produced by the liver.

Ceruloplasmin Biosynthesis. Although much is known of the general nature of ceruloplasmin (17) and its relationship to serum copper in health and disease (2, 3), the site of its synthesis has not hitherto been demonstrated. Because ceruloplasmin is an α_2-β-globulin, one might suspect the normal liver of producing ceruloplasmin. The progressive percentage enrichment of the α_2-β-globulin region of plasma proteins with Cu^{64} in the course of a 5-hour isolated rat liver perfusion is strong evidence in favor of this conjecture. This is all the more impressive, since in plasma obtained from an eviscerated surviving rat, 5 hours after a parenteral dose of Cu^{64}, the pattern of Cu^{64} distribution in the plasma proteins was indistinguishable from that of the zero time plasma specimen of the liver perfusion. In other words, it is only in the presence of a functioning liver that Cu^{64}, which at first is largely associated with the albumin fraction (4, 17), later becomes more prominently associated with the α_2-β-globulin fractions (presumably as ceruloplasmin).

The greater association of Cu^{64} activity with the α_2-β-globulin region is already detectable at 2 hours and much more prominent at 5 hours. This recalls the fact that C^{14}–labeled plasma proteins produced by the isolated perfused liver or the intact animal appear only after a lag period of 30 minutes to 1-1/2 hours (25).

A word of comment on the high Cu^{64} content of the bile seems justifiable, since the exact chemical form of copper excreted in the bile has not been determined. The possibility that ceruloplasmin or some copper-containing metabolite of ceruloplasmin is normally excreted in the bile has not been carefully examined. The abnormal elevation of the serum ceruloplasmin level in acute biliary obstruction (7), and the abnormally low serum ceruloplasmin seen in some cases of advanced liver disease, particularly Wilson's disease (2, 3), are in keeping with the liver being the site of ceruloplasmin synthesis and excretion.

Fibrinogen Biosynthesis. In our report with Bly, Watson, and Bale (25), it was clearly indicated that, on the basis of lysine-C^{14} incorporation, the liver progressively incorporated lysine-C^{14} into fibrinogen isolated as fibrin; furthermore, in experiments with the eviscerated surviving rat and the perfused hind quarters of the rat containing all abdominal viscera except the liver, no significant incorporation into fibrinogen was observed. In the light of those studies, it is difficult to accept the opinion of McFarlane in a recent authoritative review (19):

> The sites of formation of the various clotting factors, and the metabolic requirements involved are still matters of conjecture. It has long been supposed that the liver is concerned with the production of fibrinogen, but the evidence is not con-

clusive, since the experimental procedures used in animals to damage the liver or to isolate it from the circulation may well have caused greatly increased fibrinolysis, and the observed fall in fibrinogen may have been due to increased destruction rather than to decreased production.

Our studies briefly described above on the net biosynthesis of fibrinogen by the isolated perfused liver demonstrate that under the stimulus of hypofibrinogenemia the isolated perfused liver is capable of elaborating fibrinogen at rates three to four times that normally necessary for fibrinogen turnover in the intact animal. These rates are substantially greater than those described by Barnabei (1) in confirming our unpublished observations on fibrinogen biosynthesis by the isolated liver.

The view that this is true net biosynthesis of fibrinogen is supported by a variety of ancillary observations. Fibrinogen biosynthesis is suppressed in the presence of metabolic analogs, such as L-ethionine and puromycin, most markedly by the latter in spite of the maximal stimulus for production. Mitomycin C, which is believed to interfere with biosynthetic processes in the nucleus, also caused some suppression of fibrinogen biosynthesis. The isolated perfused liver in the presence of any of the three inhibitors used continues to function in an apparently normal manner in terms of bile secretion, linear urea production, amino acid oxidation, and glucose utilization. The effects of these inhibitors on the biosynthesis of the other plasma proteins will be described elsewhere.

From a strict biochemical point of view a clear-cut definition of the role of the liver in the biosynthesis of any particular plasma protein can be made only when the particular protein has been clearly and cleanly isolated, as in the case of fibrinogen. The practical difficulties of effecting such isolations on a small scale from isotopic labeling studies of the plasma proteins, such as we have described, seriously militate against such a detailed demonstration at present. The use of fractionation techniques with greater resolving power such as acrylamide gel electrophoresis already show some promise in our laboratory toward affording a more definitive picture of the biosynthetic role of the liver and the nonhepatic tissues in plasma protein production.

A final comment may be made concerning the very small, perhaps quantitatively insignificant but readily detectable protein labeling found in the α-globulin fractions and in the albumin region in experiments with the eviscerated surviving rat and the hepatectomized rat. It is possible that these activities are associated with an artefactual entrainment of labeled γ- or β-globulins by the faster moving protein fractions. A more reasonable speculation, however, would invoke the known fact that the plasma normally contains a great variety of enzyme proteins which are synthesized by the various tissues in the body. One need mention only the lactic acid dehydrogenase isoenzymes, the phosphatases, muscle and liver aldolase, plasma pepsinogen, etc.

Summary

The isolated perfused rat liver, the eviscerated surviving rat, and the hepatectomized rat have been used in studies with lysine-6-C^{14}, acetate-1-C^{14}, and S^{35}-labeled sulfate. Plasma proteins obtained from such experimental preparations have been separated by starch-block zone electrophoresis. The electrophoretic fractions have, in turn, been further fractionated by perchlorid acid (final concentration, 0.64N) to give crude serum mucoprotein fractions. The resulting mucoprotein fractions from the perfused liver studies show extensive labeling in a pattern indicating that the mucoprotein fractions are grossly heterogeneous. This view was more graphically confirmed by autoradiography of plasma proteins labeled with sulfur-35 sulfate. In no experiment with the eviscerated surviving rat or hepatectomized rat was any evidence obtained for significant incorporation of isotopically labeled metabolites into the plasma mucoprotein fractions by nonhepatic tissues. One must conclude that in the normal rat or the tumor-bearing rat the plasma mucoproteins are exclusively synthesized by the liver.

Cu^{64} acetate has been used to evaluate the role of isolated perfused liver and eviscerated surviving rat in ceruloplasmin synthesis. Preparative electrophoresis of plasma from a 5-hour liver perfusion reveals increasing association of Cu^{64} with the α_2-β-globulin fractions, presumably indicating ceruloplasmin synthesis. Similar fractionation of plasma from the eviscerated surviving rat 4-1/2 hours after a similar dose of Cu^{64} acetate showed Cu^{64} primarily associated with the albumin fraction, a pattern identical with that seen in the zero time control plasma from the liver perfusion. These observations support the view that the liver is the site of ceruloplasmin synthesis.

The exclusive role of the liver in the biosynthesis of fibrinogen, questioned by some, has been reaffirmed in isolated liver perfusion experiments in which maximal net biosynthesis of fibrinogen of 0.6 mg. per hour per gram wet weight of liver occurs. This approximates three to four times the normal rate of fibrinogen biosynthesis in turnover in the intact normal rat and occurs only in liver perfusions in which the stimulus of extreme hypofibrinogenemia associated with the use of completely defibrinated blood is present.

Acknowledgment

The authors acknowledge the technical assistance of Carmela Santomieri, Drusilla Wemett, Sarah Hallagan, Marcelle Hamshire, Elvira Di Ferrante, and Gilda Wolk. They are greatly indebted to Leon Schwartz and Gerald Cooper for their preparation of the illustrations.

They are indebted to Alec G. Bearn, Rockefeller Institute for Medical Research, for collaboration in preliminary studies and for valuable discussion of the problems in ceruloplasmin metabolism.

Literature Cited

(1) Barnabei, O., Ann Univ. Ferrara 2, 83 (1958).
(2) Bearn, A. G., Am. J. Med. 22, 747 (1957).

(3) Bearn, A. G., Kunkel, H. G., J. Clin. Invest. 31, 616 (1952); 33, 400 (1954).
(4) Bearn, A. G., Kunkel, H. G., Proc. Soc. Exptl. Biol. Med. 85, 44 (1954).
(5) Bearn, A. G., Kunkel, H. G., Slater, R. J., Am. J. Med. 21, 3 (1956).
(6) Coburn, A. F., Moore, L. V., Haninger, J., Arch. Inst. Med. 92, 185 (1953).
(7) Cummings, J. N., Goodwin, H. J., Earl, C. J., J. Clin. Pathol. 8, 69 (1955).
(8) Gordon, A. H., Biochem. J. 66, 255 (1957).
(9) Greenspan, E. M., Tepper, B., Terry, L. L., Schoenbach, E. B., J. Lab. Clin. Med. 39, 44 (1952).
(10) Haft, D. E., Miller, L. L., Am. J. Physiol. 193, 469 (1958).
(11) Haft, D. E., Roheim, P. S., White, A., Eder, H. A., J. Clin. Invest. 41, 842 (1962).
(12) Hartmann, F., Koch, H. H., Poliwoda, H., Proc. of 4th Intern. Congr. Biochem., 12-42, Vienna, 1958.
(13) Ingle, D. J., Exptl. Med. Surg. 7, 34 (1949).
(14) Keyser, J. W., J. Clin. Pathol. 5, 194 (1952).
(15) Kunkel, H. G., Slater, R. J., Proc. Soc. Exptl. Biol. Med. 72, 106 (1949).
(16) Lang. N., Renschler, H. E., Z. Ges. Exptl. Med. 130, 203 (1958).
(17) Laurell, C. B., "The Plasma Proteins," Vol. 1, pp. 360-9, F. W. Putnam, ed., Academic Press, New York, 1960.
(18) Lowry, O. H., Rosebrough, N. J., Farr, A. L., Randall, R. J., J. Biol. Chem. 193, 265 (1951).
(19) MacFarlane, R. J., "The Plasma Proteins," Vol. 2, p. 172, F. W. Putnam, ed., Academic Press, New York, 1960.
(20) Marsh, J. B., Whereat, A. F., J. Biol. Chem. 234, 3196 (1959).
(21) Meehan, F. P., Am. J. Physiol. 179, 282 (1954).
(22) Mehl, J. W., Humphrey, J., Winzler, R. J., Proc. Soc. Exptl. Biol. Med. 72, 106 (1949).
(23) Miller, L. L., Bale, W. F., J. Exptl. Med. 99, 125 (1954).
(24) Miller, L. L., Bly, C. G., Bale, W. F., Ibid., 99, 133 (1954).
(25) Miller, L. L., Bly, C. G., Watson, M. L., Bale, W. F., Ibid., 95, 531 (1951).
(26) Miller, L. L., Burke, W. T., Haft, D. E., "Some Aspects of Amino Acid Supplementation," pp. 44-59, Rutgers University Press, 1956.
(27) Roheim, P. S., Haft, D. E., White, A., Eder, H. A., Circulation 20, 968 (1959).
(28) Schmidt, K. J., J. Am. Chem. Soc. 75, 2532 (1953).
(29) Seibert, F. B., Nelson, J. W., Seibert, M. V., Arch Biochem. 18, 279 (1948).
(30) Shaber, G. S., Miller, L. L., Proc. Soc. Exptl. Biol. Med. 113, 346 (1963).
(31) Sternlieb, I., Morell, A. G., Tucker, W. D., Greene, M. W., Scheinberg, I. H., J. Clin. Invest. 6, 1834 (1961).
(32) Tiselius, A., Kabat, E. A., J. Exptl. Med. 69, 119 (1939).
(33) Van Slyke, D. D., Plazin, J., Weisiger, J. R., J. Biol. Chem. 191, 299 (1951).
(34) Winzler, R. J., "Methods of Biochemical Analysis," Vol. II, pp. 279-311, Interscience, New York, 1955.
(35) Winzler, R. J., Devor, A. W., Mehl, J. W., Smyth, I. M., J. Clin. Invest. 27, 609, 617 (1944).

Received November 30, 1962.

Studies performed under contract with the Atomic Energy Commission at the University of Rochester Atomic Energy Project, Rochester, N. Y., aided in part by a research grant from the Medical Research and Development Board, Office of the Surgeon General, Department of the Army, under contract No. DA-49-007-MD-451, and by a grant from the Jane Coffin Childs Memorial Fund for Medical Research. Presented in part at the 3rd International Congress of Biochemistry, Brussels, 1955, the 5th International Congress of Biochemistry, Moscow, 1961, and the 66th Congress of the German Society for Internal Medicine, Wiesbaden, 1960.

Protein Biosynthesis
Aminoacyl Transfer from sRNA to Ribosomes

KIVIE MOLDAVE

*Department of Biochemistry, Tufts University,
School of Medicine, Boston, Mass.*

The aminoacyl transfer reaction, one of the latter stages in protein synthesis, involves incorporation of amino acids from soluble ribonucleic acid–amino acid into ribosomal protein. This reaction requires guanosine triphosphate and a soluble portion of the cell. Evidence has been obtained with rat liver preparations that aminoacyl transfer is catalyzed by two protein factors, aminoacyl transferases (or polymerases) I and II, which have been resolved and partially purified from the soluble fraction. Transferase II activity has also been obtained from deoxycholate-soluble extracts of microsomes. With purified transferases I and II, incorporation is observed with relatively low levels of GTP; its sulfhydryl requirement is met by a variety of compounds. The characteristics of this purified amino acid incorporating system, in terms of dependency on the concentration of its components, are described.

The synthesis of proteins, as characterized by the in vitro incorporation of amino acids into the protein component of cytoplasmic ribonucleoprotein, is known to require the nonparticulate portion of the cytoplasm, ATP (adenosine triphosphate) and GTP (guanosine triphosphate) (15, 23). The initial reactions involve the carboxyl activation of amino acids in the presence of amino acid-activating enzymes (aminoacyl sRNA synthetases) and ATP, to form enzyme-bound aminoacyl adenylates and the enzymatic transfer of the aminoacyl moiety from aminoacyl adenylates to soluble ribonucleic acid (sRNA) which results in the formation of specific RNA-amino acid complexes—see, for example, reviews by Hoagland (12) and Berg (1). The subsequent steps in protein synthesis involve an interaction between aminoacyl sRNA and cytoplasmic ribonucleoprotein (ribosomes) which results in the transfer of the aminoacyl moiety to a protein-bound form (2–11, 13, 14, 18–22, 24).

Studies in this laboratory for the past several years have been concerned with the elucidation of the latter steps in this series of reactions. Specifically, efforts have been directed toward the characterization of the reaction involving the transfer of aminoacyl sRNA to mammalian ribonucleoprotein particles, the enzymatic and cofactor requirements, and possible intermediates in this process. The evidence obtained indicates that aminoacyl transfer is an enzymatic reaction requiring at least two enzyme fractions, which have been resolved and partially purified, GTP and a sulfhydryl compound; further, the possibility exists that a ribosome-bound sRNA-amino acid (or peptide) compound is formed as an intermediate in this reaction.

This report summarizes some of the properties of this system. The characterization studies described in detail were carried out with lower concentrations of ribosomes and of highly labeled aminoacyl sRNA than used previously and may therefore vary quantitatively in some respects from those reported previously (6, 7, 8).

Experimentally, C^{14}-aminoacyl sRNA was incubated with rat liver microsomes or ribosomes, GTP, various fractions obtained from the nonparticulate portion of rat liver homogenates, and buffered salt-sucrose medium in a total volume of approximately 2 ml. (6–10). The C^{14}-aminoacyl sRNA was prepared by the phenol-extraction procedure from the "pH 5 amino acid–activating enzymes" fraction of rat liver after incubation with C^{14}-L-amino acids (9, 13). C^{14}-leucyl sRNA (approximately 1000 c.p.m.), having a specific radioactivity of approximately 55,000 c.p.m. per mg. of RNA, and containing a complement of endogenous, unlabeled, bound amino acids, was used in most of these studies. The microsomes were sedimented from the post-mitochondrial supernatant at 104,000 × g (10) and the ribosomes were prepared from them by extraction with deoxycholate (16).

Figure 1 represents a schematic illustration of the separation of ribosomes, sRNA, and the enzymes involved in the transfer reaction, described in detail below. At the end of the incubation period, the ribonucleoprotein and supernatant fractions were separated by ultracentrifugation, the perchloric acid–insoluble fraction was prepared from each, and the nucleic acids and proteins were isolated from the acid-insoluble residue (17).

General Requirements for Aminoacyl Transfer

Previous studies by Hoagland et al. (13), Zamecnik et al. (24), and in this laboratory (9, 10) demonstrated that the transfer of amino acid from isolated sRNA–amino acid to microsomes required GTP, ATP, an ATP-generating system, and a soluble portion of the cell. Most of the aminoacyl-transferring activity present in the homogenate supernatant was recovered in the "pH 5 Supernatant" obtained after precipitation of the amino acid–activating enzymes at pH 5. A protein fraction, 500- to

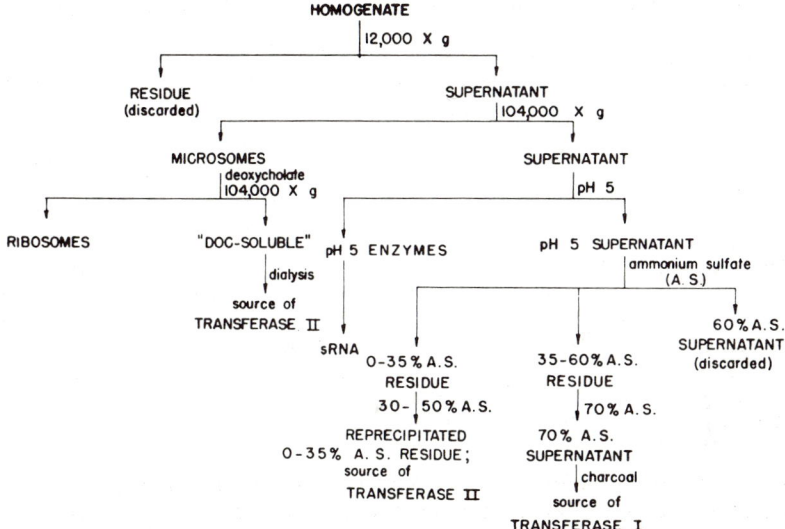

Figure 1. Scheme of fractionation

1000-fold purified, was isolated from the pH 5 Supernatant by fractionation with ammonium sulfate and charcoal (10). Table I summarizes the requirements for aminoacyl transfer to microsomes in the presence of pH 5 Supernatant and the purified transferring enzyme. Incubations with pH 5 Supernatant required ATP and GTP for maximal transfer; however, in experiments with the purified transferase, the requirement for GTP was absolute and the guanosine nucleotide was not replaced by ATP. Evidence was obtained that GTP was the only essential nucleotide required for aminoacyl transfer and that the effect of other nucleotides, such as ATP, was a reflection of their ability to generate GTP (10).

The constancy in the ratios of the specific transferring activities with respect to several amino acids (three of which are presented in

Table I. Aminoacyl Transfer to Microsomes with Crude and Purified Transferring Preparations

	C.P.M. Incorporated into Protein	
Incubation Additions [a]	pH 5 Supernatant	Purified enzyme
Complete system	283	163
Minus soluble fraction	24	24
Minus ATP, PEP	11	128
Minus GTP	163	10

[a] Incubation mixtures contained C^{14}-leucyl sRNA, 7 mg. of pH 5 Supernatant protein or 0.007 mg. of purified enzyme, 4 mg. of washed microsomes, 0.5 μmole of GTP and ATP, 10 μmoles of phosphoenolpyruvic acid, and 30 μg. of crystalline pyruvate kinase.

Table II. Transfer of Various sRNA-Bound Amino Acids to Microsomal Proteins

sRNA-Bound C^{14}-Amino Acid [a]	Specific Activity [b]		Ratio [c]
	pH 5 Supernatant ($\times 10^{-3}$)	Purified enzyme	
Glycine	2.5	2.5	1000
Leucine	8.2	6.6	810
Isoleucine	6.4	4.9	770

[a] Incubation mixtures contained 0.5 μmole of GTP, 10 μmoles of ATP, 4 mg. of washed microsomes, 7 mg. of pH 5 Supernatant protein or 0.007 mg. of purified enzyme, and approximately 0.1 mg. (1000 c.p.m.) of C^{14}-glycyl sRNA, C^{14}-leucyl sRNA, or C^{14}-isoleucyl sRNA.
[b] mμ moles of amino acid transferred per mg. of protein in enzyme preparation added.
[c] Ratio of specific activities (purified enzyme to pH 5 Supernatant).

Table II) in the process of purification of the transferring factor, has suggested that this enzyme may catalyze the transfer of several or perhaps all of the sRNA-bound amino acids to microsomal proteins (10). A similar suggestion is based on the fact that the transferring activity toward several amino acids is eluted in a single peak on chromatography on DEAE-cellulose (20).

Resolution of Two Transferring Activities

Studies with ribosomes indicated that, in contrast to experiments with microsomes, the purified transferring enzyme described above failed to catalyze aminoacyl transfer (Table III); however, the crude pH 5 Supernatant was active with both particle preparations. As described in Table IV, when the incubations with purified enzyme (transferase I) were supplemented with the dialyzed deoxycholate-soluble microsomal extract (transferase II) obtained during the isolation of ribosomes (Figure 1), transferring activity was restored (6, 7). Glutathione was also

Table III. Aminoacyl Transfer to Intact Rat Liver Microsomes and to Ribosomes

Incubation Additions [a]	C.P.M. Incorporated into Protein	
	Microsomes	Ribosomes
None	0	0
pH 5 Supernatant	218	120
pH 5 Supernatant, minus GTP	128	63
Purified enzyme	163	0

[a] Incubation mixtures contained C^{14}-leucyl sRNA, 7 mg. of pH 5 Supernatant protein or 0.007 mg. of purified enzyme, 4 mg. of washed microsomes or 2 mg. of ribosomes, 0.5 μmole of GTP, and 10 μmoles of ATP.

Table IV. Effect of Soluble and Microsomal Extracts on Aminoacyl Transfer

Incubation Additions [a]	C.P.M. Incorporated into Protein
pH 5 Supernatant	268
Transferase I	4
+ GSH	28
Microsomal transferase II	0
+ GSH	0
Transferases I and II	46
+ GSH	273

[a] Incubation mixtures contained C^{14}-leucyl sRNA, 7 mg. of ribosomes, 1 μmole of GTP, approximately 7 mg. of pH 5 Supernatant protein, 0.007 mg. of transferase I protein, 1.2 mg. of microsomal transferase II protein, and 10 μmoles of glutathione where indicated.

required in the presence of the combined fractions but was inactive in the absence of either one of these preparations. Thus, the protein fraction purified from the pH 5 Supernatant which is active in experiments with microsomes, has been designated as aminoacyl transferase (or polymerase) I; the deoxycholate-soluble fraction, referred to here as microsomal transferase (or polymerase) II, was not active by itself or with glutathione.

Since pH 5 Supernatant was active in the transfer of sRNA–bound amino acids, it suggested that both of the essential fractions described above were also present in this crude soluble preparation. Experimental verification of this suggestion is presented in Table V (8). Fractionation of the pH 5 Supernatant with ammonium sulfate yielded two fractions, 0 to 35% A.S. residue and 35 to 60% A.S. residue, which by themselves catalyzed aminoacyl transfer in the presence of glutathione. Reprecipitation of the 0 to 35% A.S. fraction, as described in Figure 1,

Table V. Effect of Various Ammonium Sulfate Fractions on Aminoacyl Transfer

Incubation Additions [a]	C.P.M. Incorporated into Protein
0-35% A.S. residue	140
35-60% A.S. residue	191
Reprecipitated 0-35% A.S. fraction	29
+ transferase I	130
+ transferase II	33
Reprecipitated 35-60% A.S. fraction	36
+ transferase I	44
+ transferase II	282

[a] Incubations were carried out with 3 mg. of ribosomes, C^{14}-leucyl sRNA, 1 μmole of GTP, 10 μmoles of glutathione, and 5 mg. of protein of initial 0-35% A.S. residue, 6 mg. of protein of 35-60% A.S. residue, 3 mg. of reprecipitated 0-35% A.S. fraction protein, 4 mg. of reprecipitated 35-60% A.S. fraction protein, 0.003 mg. of purified transferase I protein, or 0.4 mg. of microsomal transferase II protein where indicated.

or partial purification by stepwise additions of ammonium sulfate (between 30 and 40 or 40 and 50% saturation) yielded a preparation labeled reprecipitated 0 to 35% A.S. fraction, which was usually inactive in the absence of purified transferase I; the addition of microsomal transferase II to this preparation had no effect. Occasionally, preparations of soluble transferase II were obtained at this step which were contaminated with, and could not easily be resolved from, transferase I activity. Reprecipitation of the 35 to 60% A.S. residue with ammonium sulfate at pH 6.5 to 7.0 (8) yielded a preparation which was inactive by itself or in the presence of transferase I, purified as described in Figure 1, but which required microsomal or soluble transferase II for activity. Thus, it appeared that the subfractions obtained from the initial 0 to 35% A.S. residue, designated here soluble transferase (or polymerase) II, and the fraction prepared from microsomes by extraction with deoxycholate were equivalent and required the transferase I activity for aminoacyl transfer. The activities designated transferase I and II (microsomal and soluble) are heat-labile, nondialyzable, and salt-precipitable, suggesting that they are enzymatic in nature.

Aminoacyl transferase I represents a highly purified (500- to 1000-fold) preparation of the initial 35 to 60% A.S. residue described above, obtained from the pH 5 Supernatant by further fractionation with ammo-

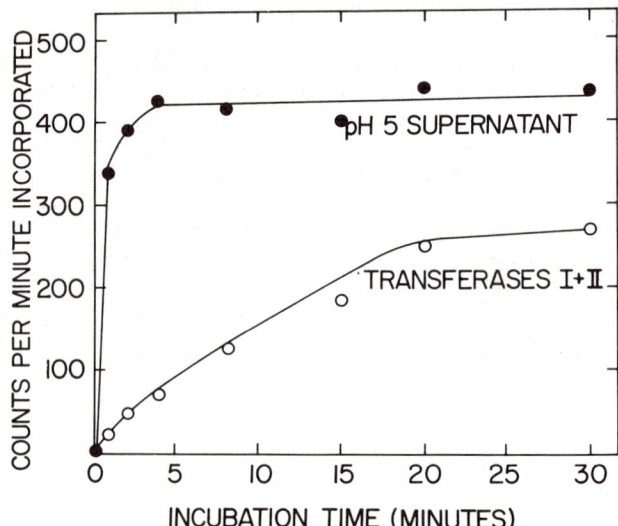

Figure 2. Time-dependent transfer of amino acids to protein in presence of pH 5 Supernatant or transferases I and II

Incubations carried out with C^{14}-leucyl sRNA (1500 c.p.m.), 0.8 mg. of ribosomes, 10 mg. of pH 5 Supernatant protein (●), or 0.003 mg. of transferase I plus 2 mg. of solable transferase II protein (○), and other components as described in text

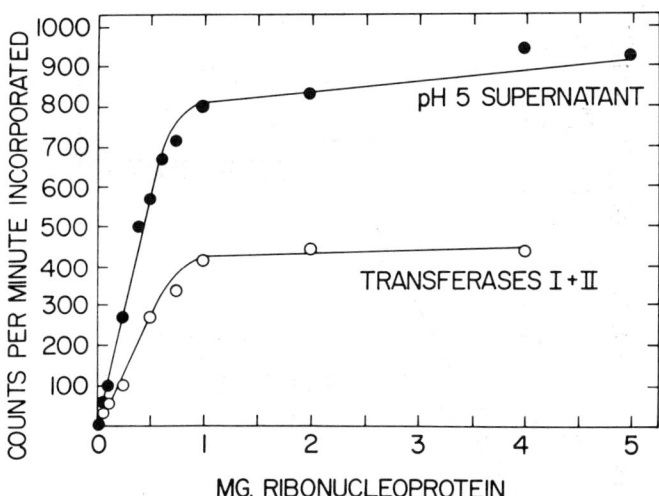

Figure 3. Effect of ribosomal concentration on aminoacyl transfer to protein

All incubations contained C^{14}-leucyl sRNA (2000 c.p.m.), 10 mg. of pH 5 Supernatant protein (●) or 0.003 mg. of transferase I plus 2 mg. of soluble transferase II protein (○), ribosomal concentrations indicated, and other components as described in text

nium sulfate and charcoal (10). It is stable frozen for several months. Transferase I is relatively heat-stable in the presence of the buffered salt-sucrose medium used (10); however, after dialysis against 0.02M phosphate buffer, the activity is lost within 10 minutes at 60° (6). Microsomal transferase II, although relatively low in protein, did not lend itself to further purification because of its extreme lability; it is stable frozen for less than a week. Soluble transferase II was obtained approximately 50-fold purified by subfractionation of the initial 0 to 35% A.S. residue as described above (8); it is stable frozen for approximately 3 weeks.

Characteristics of Reaction

The time-dependent incorporation of amino acid into ribosomal protein is shown in Figure 2. When the crude pH 5 Supernatant fraction was used, incorporation was very rapid and essentially complete in 2 to 4 minutes. Incorporation was usually slower when the more purified enzyme fractions, transferases I and II, were used; incorporation was complete after approximately 20 minutes. A similar rate of incorporation was observed when the transferase II used was isolated either from the microsomes or the post-microsomal supernatant.

The extent of amino acid incorporation was also found to be dependent on ribosomal and aminoacyl sRNA concentrations. Figure 3 il-

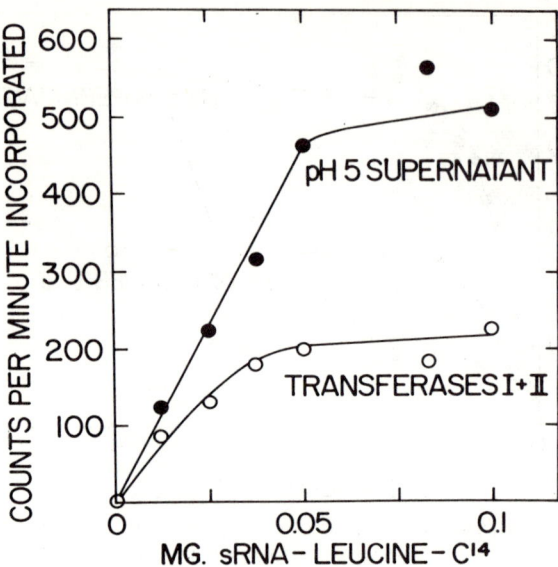

Figure 4. Effect of sRNA-amino acid concentration on aminoacyl transfer to protein

Incubations consisted of 0.8 mg. of ribosomes, 10 mg. of pH 5 Supernatant protein (●) or 0.003 mg. of transferase Ip lus 2 mg. of soluble transferase II protein (○), amounts of C -leucyl sRNA incicated, and other components as described in text

lustrates the effect of ribosomal concentration on aminoacyl transfer in the presence of pH 5 Supernatant or transferases I and II. The incorporation of amino acid was linear below 1 mg. of ribosomes and the specific radioactivities were greater than that above 1 mg. The relative incorporation of C^{14} with varying ribosomal concentrations was similar with the crude and the more purified enzyme preparations, although with the particular preparations used in this experiment, the total radioactivity incorporated differed. It has been shown in this laboratory (6) that with relatively higher concentrations of C^{14}-leucyl sRNA of lower specific activity, the total C^{14} incorporated was also dependent on ribosomal concentrations and was linear over a range of from 2 to 7 mg. Figure 4 shows that at optimal enzyme concentrations and 0.25 mg. of ribonucleoprotein per ml. of incubation mixture, the amount of C^{14} incorporated was dependent on the concentration of aminoacyl sRNA added and was linear at lower concentrations. Concentrations between 20 and 30 μg. of sRNA—amino acid appeared to be optimal.

Aminoacyl transfer was found to be optimal with about 10 mg. of added pH 5 Supernatant protein. At much higher concentrations of this preparation, inhibition of amino acid incorporation was observed. When

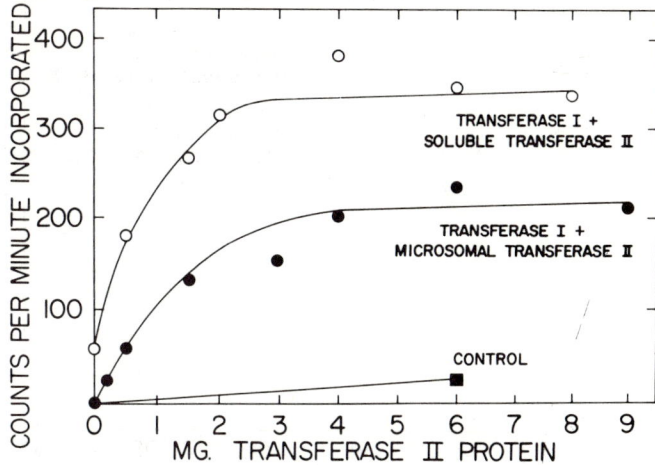

Figure 5. Dependence of aminoacyl transfer on varying concentrations of transferases I and II

Incubations contained 0.7 mg. of ribosomes, C^{14}-leucyl sRNA (1200 c.p.m.), 0.005 mg. of transferase I protein and amounts of soluble (○) or microsomal (●) transferase II protein, and other components as described in text. Control incubations (■) carried out in absence of transferase I

the more purified transferases I and II were used, as illustrated in Figure 5, optimal incorporation was achieved at much lower concentrations of added soluble protein (6, 8). The addition of either transferase I or transferase II alone to this incubation (lower curve, Control) did not catalyze aminoacyl transfer. In the presence of transferase I, incorporation was dependent on the concentration of transferase II. Similar results were obtained when transferase II was assayed for transfer activity as a function of the concentration of transferase I. Significant incorporation was obtained when 0.5 mg. of ribosomal transferase II was incubated in the presence of 5 µg. of transferase I. Optimal incorporation occurred with 4.0 mg. of added microsomal transferase II. In the presence of 3 µg. of transferase I, 2.0 mg. of soluble transferase II resulted in optimal incorporation of amino acid, with more total radiocarbon being incorporated than when microsomal transferase II was used. As with the crude enzyme preparation, it was observed that the addition of relatively large amounts of transferring preparations, not shown here, tended to inhibit the incorporation of amino acids from sRNA into ribosomal protein.

Previous studies demonstrated that GTP was the only essential nucleotide in the aminoacyl transfer reaction (**2, 10, 21, 22**). The effect of varying concentrations of GTP on this reaction is presented in Figure 6. Maximum incorporation was obtained with as little as 0.05 µmole of GTP per ml. in incubations with transferase I and soluble transferase II. When microsomal transferase II was used, the requirement for

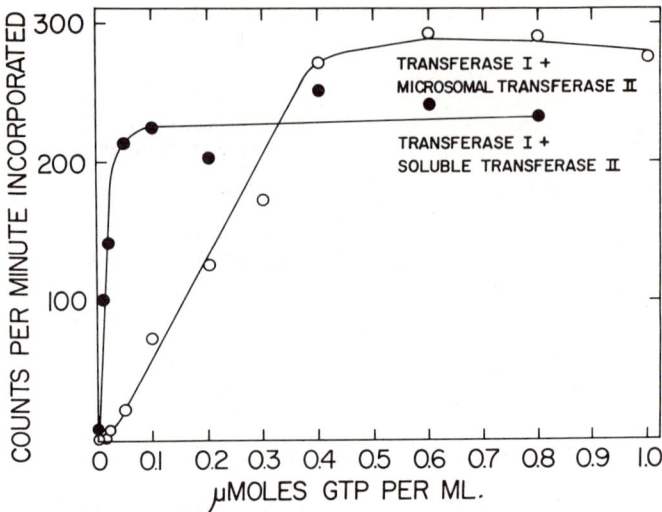

Figure 6. Effect of GTP on aminoacyl transfer to protein

Incubations with C^{14}-leucyl sRNA (800 c.p.m.), 0.6 mg. of ribosomes, 10 µmoles of glutathione, and amounts of GTP indicated also contained 0.003 mg. of transferase I protein and 4 mg. of soluble (●) or 2 mg. of microsomal (○) transferase II protein

GTP was greater and at least 0.4 µmole of GTP per ml. was required for optimal activity. Although not shown here, inhibition of the transfer reaction with microsomal transferase II was observed with about

Table VI. Effect of Various Sulfhydryl Compounds on Aminoacyl Transfer

Incubation Additions [a]	Per Cent Stimulation [b]
Glutathione	140
Cysteine	187
2,3-Dimercaptopropanol	153
Coenzyme A	160
Mercaptoethanol	174
Thioglycollate	146

[a] Incubation mixtures contained C^{14}-leucyl sRNA, 1 µmole of GTP, 4 mg. of ribosomes, 0.005 mg. of transferase I protein, and 0.7 mg. of transferase II protein.
[b] Per cent increase in specific radioactivity (c.p.m. per mg.) of ribosomal protein over that observed in absence of sulfhydryl compound.

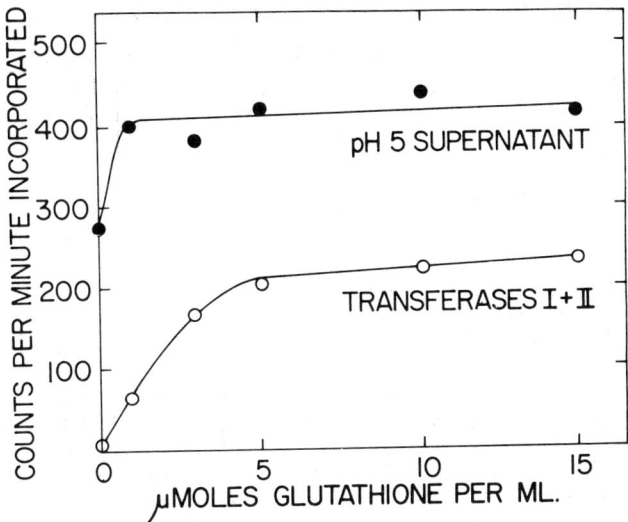

Figure 7. Effect of glutathione on aminoacyl transfer to protein

Incubations consisted of C^{14}-leucyl sRNA (1500 c.p.m.), 0.8 mg. of ribosomes, 0.5 µmole of GTP, 10 mg. of pH 5 Supernatant protein (●), or 0.003 mg. of transferase I plus 2 mg. of soluble transferase II protein (○), and amounts of glutathione indicated

1 µmole of GTP per ml. No such inhibition was seen when soluble transferase II was used. At suboptimal concentrations of microsomal transferase II, incorporation of amino acid was found to be maximal when lower concentrations of GTP (0.1 µmole per ml.) were added. This observation might reflect the presence of significant GTP-ase activity in this enzyme fraction as compared to soluble transferase II.

It has been reported that glutathione plays a role in the transfer of amino acids from sRNA to ribosomal protein (2, 4, 6, 8, 14, 19). The requirement for glutathione in this rat-liver system is illustrated in Figure 7. Some preparations of pH 5 Supernatant were dependent on the presence of glutathione for maximal activity, although preparations have been obtained which exhibited no such requirement. Glutathione was mandatory for amino acid incorporation with purified transferase I and either soluble or microsomal transferase II. A glutathione concentration of about 2.5 to 5.0 µmoles per ml. was found to be optimal with both of these preparations. In order to determine whether the stimulatory effect observed with glutathione was due to this specific peptide or to a general sulfhydryl requirement, a variety of different sulfhydryl-containing compounds were tested for their ability to replace glutathione (Table VI). All the compounds tested were found to be effective in promoting aminoacyl transfer (8).

Table VII. Transfer of Various sRNA-Bound Amino Acids

sRNA-Bound C^{14}-Amino Acid [a]	C.P.M. Added per Incubation	C.P.M. Incorporated into Protein
Alanine	644	65
Aspartic acid	1022	132
Glycine	715	73
Leucine	637	146
Lysine	760	116
Phenylalanine	604	58
Threonine	1279	215
Valine	1588	277
Amino acid mixture	2463	125

[a] Incubation mixtures contained 3 mg. of ribosomes, 0.007 mg. of transferase I protein, 4 mg. of soluble transferase II protein, approximately 0.05 mg. of aminoacyl sRNA, 1 μmole of GTP, and 10 μmoles of glutathione. Results obtained when transferases I and II were replaced by pH 5 Supernatant were quantitatively similar.

Incubations of crude pH 5 Supernatant with several C^{14}-aminoacyl sRNA preparations, differing only in the nature of the C^{14}-amino acid, showed that all amino acids tested were incorporated into ribosomal protein. With combined transferases I and II, the results presented in Table VII indicated that all of the amino acids tested were also incorporated in the presence of these purified fractions (8). When either of the transferases was omitted from these incubations, little amino acid transfer was observed with any of the C^{14}-aminoacyl sRNA preparations. Variations in total amounts of C^{14} incorporated, as shown here, are probably due to variations in the specific radioactivity of the various sRNA-bound amino acids used. These purified transferase preparations did not catalyze the incorporation of free amino acids into sRNA or ribosomes.

Summary

The transfer of labeled amino acids from aminoacyl sRNA to purified rat-liver ribonucleoprotein particles has been shown to require GTP, and a soluble portion (pH 5 Supernatant) of the cell. An enzyme fraction, aminoacyl transferase (or polymerase) I, purified from the pH 5 Supernatant was found to catalyze the transfer of amino acid to protein with microsomes, but not with the more purified ribonucleoprotein particles (ribosomes). When transferase I was supplemented with glutathione and a microsomal extract, microsomal aminoacyl transferase (or polymerase) II, transferring activity was restored. Since the pH 5 Supernatant was active in catalyzing the transfer of amino acids from sRNA to ribosomal protein, it was concluded that both transferring activities were present in this crude fraction. Resolution of the two activities from the pH 5 Supernatant fraction was obtained by salt-fractionation procedures. Neither enzyme fraction was active when incubated individually or with glutathione, but together in the presence of sulfhydryl compound, they catalyzed aminoacyl transfer to ribosomal protein. Thus, transferase II has been partially purified from the cellular supernatant and was also found in deoxycholate extracts of microsomes.

The transfer of amino acids from sRNA to protein was dependent on the concentration of ribosomes, aminoacyl sRNA, and transferring enzymes. Aminoacyl transfer was observed with less than 0.05 μ mole of GTP per ml., and the reaction exhibited a sulfhydryl requirement which was met by a variety of compounds. Transfer of several sRNA-bound C^{14}-amino acids to ribosomal protein was observed with the purified transferases I and II.

Acknowledgment

The collaboration of June M. Fessenden, Lois Grossi, Judith Cairncross, Saul Slapikoff, Richard Sutter, and Mervyn Weiner in various phases of this investigation is gratefully acknowledged.

Literature Cited

(1) Berg. P., Ann. Rev. Biochem. 30, 293 (1961).
(2) Bishop, J. O., Schweet, R. S., Biochim. Biophys. Acta 49, 235 (1961).
(3) Decken, A. von der, Campbell, P. N., Biochem. J. 82, 448 (1962).
(4) Decken, A. von der, Hultin, T., Biochim. Biophys. Acta 45, 139 (1960).
(5) Ehrenstein, G. von, Lipmann, F., Proc. Natl. Acad. Sci. U.S. 47, 941 (1961).
(6) Fessenden, J. M., Moldave, K., Biochemistry 1, 485 (1962).
(7) Fessenden, J. M., Moldave, K., Biochem. Biophys. Research Communs. 6, 232 (1961).
(8) Fessenden, J. M., Moldave, K., J. Biol. Chem. 238, 1479 (1963).
(9) Grossi, L. G., Moldave, K., Biochim. Biophys. Acta 35, 275 (1959).
(10) Grossi, L. G., Moldave, K., J. Biol. Chem. 235, 2370 (1960).
(11) Hirokawa, R., Omori, S., Takahashi, T., Ogata, K., Biochim. Biophys. Acta 49, 614 (1961).
(12) Hoagland, M. B., in "The Nucleic Acids," Vol. III, p. 349, E. Chargaff and J. N. Davidson, eds., Academic Press, New York, 1960.
(13) Hoagland, M. B., Stephenson, M. L., Scott, J. F., Hecht, L. I., Zamecnik, P. C., J. Biol. Chem. 231, 241 (1958).
(14) Hülsmann, W. C., Lipmann, F., Biochim. Biophys. Acta 43, 129 (1960).
(15) Keller, E. B., Zamecnik, P. C., J. Biol. Chem. 221, 45 (1956).
(16) Kirsch, J. F., Siekevitz, P., Palade, G. E., Ibid., 235, 1419 (1960).
(17) Moldave, K., Ibid., 235, 2365 (1960).
(18) Nathans, D., Ann. N. Y. Acad. Sci. 88, 718 (1960).
(19) Nathans, D., Lipmann, F., Biochim. Biophys. Acta 43, 126 (1960).
(20) Nathans, D., Lipmann, F., Proc. Natl. Acad. Sci. U. S. 47, 497 (1961).
(21) Takanami, M., Biochim. Biophys. Acta 51, 85 (1961).
(22) Takanami, M., Okamoto, T., Ibid., 44, 379 (1960).
(23) Zamecnik, P. C., Keller, E. B., J. Biol. Chem. 209, 337 (1954).
(24) Zamecnik, P. C., Stephenson, M. L., Hecht, L. I., Proc. Natl. Acad. Sci. U. S. 44, 73 (1958).

Received April 26, 1963. Work supported by the American Cancer Society (Research Grant P-177) and the U.S. Public Health Service (Research Grant AM 01397 and Research Career Program Award K3-GM-4124).

4
Refractive Indices of Amino Acids, Proteins, and Related Substances

THOMAS L. McMEEKIN, MERTON L. GROVES, AND NORBERT J. HIPP

Eastern Regional Research Laboratory, Philadelphia 18, Pa.

> The molar refractions of the amino acids were determined by measurements on their aqueous solutions and the expanded Lorenz-Lorentz equation. The refractive indices of a number of proteins were calculated from their amino acid compositions and the values for the refraction of the amino acid residues. These calculated results are in good agreement with those experimentally determined, demonstrating that refractive index is a unique characteristic of a protein. A comparison of the refractive index of heat denatured β-lactoglobulin with the native protein demonstrated that changes in structure produced a small change in refractive index, not associated with a change in volume.

Although the refractive index of a solution can be simply and precisely measured, it has been little used in characterizing proteins. The refraction of proteins is, however, frequently involved in measurements on protein solutions by such methods as light scattering, sedimentation, and electrophoresis. Previous investigations, summarized by Doty and Geiduschek (11), indicate the importance of composition, density, charge, and environmental factors in determining the refractive indices of proteins. They note that the values reported for the refractive indices of proteins are close to 1.60 and are nearly constant.

Adair and Robinson (1) indicate that the refractive index of a protein or an amino acid is approximately determined by its elementary composition; however, the structure of a molecule is also of importance. The values reported for amino acids are scattered and fragmentary (1, 10), and prior to our preliminary communication (25) no systematic investigation had accounted quantitatively for the relationship between the amino acid composition of a protein and its refractive index.

In this paper, the results of a systematic study of the refractive indices of the amino acids, and some peptides and proteins, are described. The value for the refractive index of a protein calculated from the refractive increments of its amino acid residues and solution volume agrees with the experimental value and is a characteristic of the protein. The change in the refractive index of a protein as a result of denaturation has also been investigated.

Materials and Methods

Amino Acids and Peptides. The amino acids and peptides used were high grade commercial products, further purified by recrystallization from alcohol-water mixtures, except when they were chromatographically pure. Glycolamide was prepared by passing dry ammonia into cold, freshly distilled ethyl glycollate. Pure lactamide was obtained from E. H. Harris of this laboratory.

Proteins. Crystalline lysozyme, bovine serum albumin, ribonuclease, and pepsin were obtained from the Armour Laboratories and crystalline β-lactoglobulin was prepared from skimmed milk. α-Lactalbumin was obtained from W. G. Gordon of this laboratory. Crystalline ovalbumin and human serum albumin were obtained from Nutritional Biochemical Corp. and purified pigskin gelatin from the Eastman Kodak Co.

Refractive Index Determination. The refractive indices of amino acids were determined by means of a dipping refractometer, using a sodium light, and also with the Brice-Halwer (4) differential refractometer. Concentrations of solutions were based on the dry weight of an aliquot at 110° C. and also on moisture determinations. The values obtained were in essential agreement. No difference was found between the DL-amino acids and the corresponding optically active amino acids; consequently, most of the measurements were made on the DL-amino acids. Refractive index measurements were made on solutions varying in concentration from 1 to 10%, depending on the solubility of the amino acid. No difference in refractive increment was found due to variations in concentration, except in the case of glycine solutions, where the difference could be correlated with variations in specific volume and were essentially eliminated by applying the appropriate volume for a given concentration of glycine. Cystine, tyrosine, and aspartic acid are not sufficiently soluble in water for accurate measurement of refractive indices. The molar refraction of cystine was calculated by using the molar atomic refractions (in cc.) given by Fajans (12): C 2.418, H 1.10, O^- 1.525, O^{-2} 2.211, and N 2.322, and S 8.11 given by Cohen (8). The molar refractions of tyrosine and aspartic acid were estimated from the molar refractions of glycyl tyrosine and glycyl aspartate, respectively, by subtracting the refraction due to the glycyl residue.

Protein solutions of 1 and 2% concentrations were used for making refractive index measurements. The values for water as a function of wavelength of light and temperature were taken from the International

Critical Tables and from Tilton and Taylor (32). The wavelength of light is given in millimicrons (mμ).

Calculations. Refractive Indices and Molar Refractions of Solutions of Amino Acids and Proteins. The mean refractive indices of the amino acids and proteins were calculated by means of the following expanded Lorenz-Lorentz equation as given by Doty and Geiduschek (11):

$$\frac{n^2 - 1}{n^2 + 2} = c\bar{v}\,\frac{(n_p^2 - 1)}{(n_p^2 + 2)} + (1 - c\bar{v})\,\frac{(n_0^2 - 1)}{(n_0^2 + 2)} \tag{1}$$

where n_p, n_0, and n indicate the refractive indices of the water-free protein or amino acid, the solvent and the solution respectively, $\bar{v}$ is the specific volume of the protein or amino acid and concentration, c, is expressed in grams per cubic centimeter. Molar refraction, R, is calculated by Equation 2.

$$[R] = \frac{n_p^2 - 1}{n_p^2 + 2} \times \frac{M}{\rho} \tag{2}$$

where n_p is the mean refractive index of the amino acid or protein, M, is the molecular weight of the amino acid (for proteins, 100 grams has been used instead of the molecular weight of the protein), and ρ is the density of the amino acid or protein, $1/\bar{v}$.

Refractive Index of Protein from Amino Acid Composition. The method used for calculating the refractive index of a protein from its amino acid composition is essentially the same as that described by Cohn and Edsall (9, Chap. 16) for calculating the specific volume of a protein from its amino acid composition.

The weight per cent of each amino acid found by analysis is converted into the weight per cent of its residue by multiplying by the ratio of the molecular weight of the residue (amino acid minus 1 mole of water) divided by the molecular weight of the amino acid. Then the weight per cent of each amino acid residue is multiplied by the value of the refraction of 1 gram of residue, as given in Table I, to give the total refractive volume in 100 grams of the protein due to a given amino acid residue. The total refractive volume of the amino acid residues in 100 grams of protein is obtained by adding the refractive volumes of the individual amino acid residues. Since an amino acid analysis is seldom perfect, a correction is made by multiplying the refraction per 100 grams of protein by percentage recovery, which is obtained by adding the weight percentages of amino acid residues and dividing by 100. The mean refractive index of the protein, n_p, is then calculated by solving for n_p in Equation 2, where [R] is the value obtained for the refractive volume of 100 grams of protein and M is equal to 100. Amide nitrogen is arbitrarily calculated as being combined with the glutamic acid residues; any excess is assigned to aspartic acid residues.

Table I. Refractive Indices, Molar Refractions of Amino Acids, 25°C

Amino Acid	Specific Volume[a], Cc.	Refractive Index
Glycine	0.58	1.685
Alanine	0.68	1.606
α-Aminobutyric acid	0.74	1.587
Valine	0.79	1.571
α-Aminovaleric acid [b]	0.79	1.577
Leucine	0.83	1.565
Isoleucine	0.83	1.568
α-Aminocaproic acid	0.83	1.565
Serine	0.58	1.676
Threonine	0.66	1.618
Hydroxyproline	0.64	1.618
Proline	0.70	1.596
Methionine	0.71	1.646
Cystine	0.59	–
Phenylalanine	0.74	1.682
Tyrosine	0.68	–
Tryptophan	0.71	1.754
Histidine	0.64	1.700
Arginine	0.67	1.664
Lysine	0.74	1.615
Aspartic acid	0.56	–
Glutamic acid	0.63	1.655
Asparagine	0.59	1.691
Glutamine	0.64	1.670

[a] (9).
[b] Calculated from data of Craig and Schmidt (10).
[c] 2 moles of water subtracted (7.46 cc.).

and Calculated Refractions of Amino Acid Residues
(λ = 589 mμ)

Amino Acid Observed	Residue (Ref. of Amino Acid - 3.73)	Refraction per G. Residue ($\frac{\text{Mol. Ref. Res.}}{\text{Mol. Wt. Res.}}$), Cc.
16.54 ± 0.1	12.81	0.225
20.88 ± 0.15	17.15	0.242
25.67 ± 0.15	21.94	0.258
30.46 ± 0.13	26.73	0.270
30.72 ± 0.15	26.99	0.272
35.32 ± 0.15	31.59	0.279
35.60 ± 0.20	31.87	0.282
35.17 ± 0.15	31.44	0.278
22.89 ± 0.10	19.16	0.220
27.55 ± 0.10	23.82	0.236
29.57 ± 0.10	25.84	0.229
27.47 ± 0.10	23.74	0.245
38.18 ± 0.05	34.45	0.263
56.04	48.58[c]	0.238
45.94 ± 0.15	42.21	0.287
48.07	44.34	0.272
58.97 ± 0.30	55.24	0.297
38.35 ± 0.15	34.62	0.253
43.20 ± 0.10	39.47	0.253
37.83 ± 0.2	34.10	0.266
28.54	24.81	0.216
33.80 ± 0.15	30.07	0.233
29.82 ± 0.20	26.09	0.229
34.10 ± 0.20	30.37	0.237

Results

Amino Acids. The values for the refractive indices and molar refractions of the amino acids calculated from the refractive indices by Lorenz-Lorentz Equations 1 and 2 are recorded in Table I. Values for molar refractions of the aliphatic amino acids are in good agreement with values calculated from atomic refraction factors. However, the molar refractions of tryptophan, tyrosine, phenylalanine, and histidine are larger than those calculated from atomic refraction factors and larger than might be expected from their comparative specific volumes.

The refractivity per gram of amino acid residue (Table I) is obtained from the molar refraction of the amino acid by subtracting the value of 3.73 due to the loss of a molecule of water in forming the residue from the amino acid. This value is the sum of its atomic refraction factors, $2H = 2.2$ and $O = 1.53$. It is in essential agreement with the value deduced from the molar refractions of glycine and its peptides. The molar refraction of glycine is 16.54, of diglycine 29.89, of triglycine 41.33 and of glycyl leucine 48.04 (Table III). Thus, by difference, the loss of a mole of water in making diglycine decreases molar refraction by 3.19 and the loss of 2 moles of water in making triglycine decreases refraction by 4.15 per mole of water. A value of 3.8 cc. is obtained for water in the formation of glycyl leucine, giving an average value of 3.72 for water from the three peptides.

Specific Volumes and Refractive Indices of Proteins. The specific volumes and refractive indices, as well as the refractive indices calculated from the amino acid compositions of a number of proteins, are recorded in Table II. The refractive indices calculated by using the amino acid composition of the protein are in good agreement with the values as determined in the case of most proteins, except in the cases of α-casein, gelatin, and α-lactalbumin, where the measurements were made away from the isoelectric point. This difference could be due to a charge effect, as was found by Perlmann and Longsworth (26), or to inaccurate specific volumes, since the blank correction used in specific volume calculations from density determinations is of questionable applicability on protein solutions containing alkali. The close agreement between the determined value for the refractive index of ovalbumin was unexpected, since ovalbumin contains carbohydrate and no estimate is made of the refraction due to carbohydrate. The calculated refractive index is, however, based on the assumption that ovalbumin is composed entirely of amino acid residues, which indicates that the refraction of the carbohydrate does not greatly differ from that of the average amino acid.

The importance of specific volume or density in determining refractive index is apparent in Equations 1 and 2, which are used in calculating refractive index and molar refraction. This inverse relationship between specific volume and refractive index is illustrated in Table II (cf. columns 2 and 4). The necessity of obtaining an accurate value for the specific volume of a protein in order to obtain agreement between its refractive index calculated from the amino acid composition and the determined value can be illustrated in the case of ribonu-

Table II. Specific Volumes and Refractive Indices of Proteins
25° (λ = 589 mμ)

Protein	Solvent, pH		Refraction/100 G.	Specific Volume, Cc.	Refractive Index Detd.	Refractive Index Calcd. from amino acid comp.
α-Casein	NaOH,	7.0	25.50	0.728	1.618	1.607 [a]
Gelatin	Water,	5.0	24.27	0.682	1.630	1.618 [b]
α-Lactalbumin	NaOH,	7.0	25.64	0.735	1.615	1.601 [c]
β-Lactoglobulin	0.1M NaCl,	5.2	25.44	0.751	1.594	1.590 [d]
Lysozyme	Water,	6.0	25.34	0.718	1.624	1.620 [b]
Ovalbumin	Water,	5.0	25.35	0.745	1.596	1.593 [b]
Pepsin	Water,	5.0	24.91	0.725	1.603	1.605 [e]
Ribonuclease	Water,	4.8	24.66	0.693	1.630	1.630 [f]
Bovine serum albumin	Water,	5.0	25.32	0.734	1.606	1.599 [g]
Horse serum albumin	Water,	5.0	25.12	0.734	1.600	
Human serum albumin	Water,	5.0	25.28	0.736	1.603	1.602 [b]

[a] (14); [b] (33); [c] (15); [d] (13); [e] (3); [f] (20); [g] (30).

clease, where a number of different values for its specific volume have been reported. Rothen's (28) value of 0.709 on the ribonuclease prepared by Kunitz is in good agreement with that calculated from its amino acid composition. Using ribonuclease obtained from the Armour Laboratory, Buzzell and Tanford (6) found 0.728 for its specific volume, while Harrington and Schellman (17) reported 0.692 to 0.696. Since the reported variations in the specific volume of ribonuclease are large, it was desirable to determine the specific volume on the sample used. The value of 0.695 found is in excellent agreement with the value of Harrington and Schellman (17). Its nitrogen content, found to be 16.6%, is also in agreement with 16.8% found by Harrington and Schellman. The value for the specific volume of ribonuclease of 0.693 was used in calculating its refractive index from the amino acid composition. In the case of pepsin, no value for its specific volume could be located. The specific volume of a 2% solution was found to be 0.725 cc., also in agreement with the 0.725 calculated from its amino acid composition. The remainder of the values for specific volumes given in Table II were taken from our previous compilation (24).

Refractive Indices of Peptides. To determine the effect of peptide formation on refractive index, the refractive indices of several peptides were determined (Table III). The average molar refraction of water produced in peptide formation can be estimated, empirically, by subtracting the observed molar refraction of the peptide from the sum of molar refractions of its constituent amino acids.

Tyrosine and aspartic acid are not sufficiently soluble for accurate measurements of the refractive indices of their solutions. Consequently, their molar refractions have been estimated from their more soluble glycyl peptides. From the results given in Table III, the molar refractions of tyrosine (48.07) and aspartic acid (28.54) are obtained by

Table III. Molar Refractions of Some Peptides
25° (λ = 589 mµ)

Substance	Specific Volume, Cc.	Refractive Index	Molar Refraction Obsd.	Molar Refraction Calcd. with Atomic factors
Glycine	0.581 [a]	1.685	16.54	16.38
Diglycine	0.584 [a]	1.702	29.89	29.09
Triglycine	0.600 [a]	1.649	41.33	41.38
Glycylleucine	0.741	1.606	48.04	47.52
Glycyltyrosine	0.664	1.694	60.73	54.10
Glycylaspartate	0.557	1.706	41.2	39.82

[a] (9).

subtracting the calculated molar refraction of the glycyl residue [12.66 (molar refraction of glycine minus the refraction of 1 mole of water)] from the refraction of the peptide. The molar refractions calculated for the peptides in Table III are in good agreement with the observed except in the case of the tyrosine peptide and to a lesser extent the aspartic acid peptide; consequently, it is felt that the values for the molar refraction of tyrosine and aspartic acid deduced from experimental measurements on their peptides are more accurate than the values calculated from atomic factors. Since our preliminary publication (25), the molar refractivity of glycyl aspartate has been redetermined on a highly purified sample. The value of 41.2 cc. for its molar refraction is about 2% lower than that previously reported. This has reduced the value for the molar refractivity of the aspartic acid residue from 26.06 to 24.81. Since aspartic acid is present in considerable amounts in proteins, the lowering of the value for its refractivity has slightly reduced the calculated values for the refractive indices of proteins given in Table II, as compared to the previously published values (25).

Comparison of Molar Refractions of Amino Acids with Their Uncharged Isomers. Numerous comparisons have been made between the properties of amino acids and the properties of their nonzwitterion isomers (9). By comparing the solution densities of glycine and its isomer, glycolamide, and alanine with its isomer, lactamide, it has been found that the amino acid occupies about 13 cc. per mole less volume than its uncharged isomer. Consequently, it is also of interest to compare the solution refractive indices of these amino acids with their isomers. Table IV shows that the refractive indices of the amino acids are considerably greater than those of their uncharged isomers; however, the molar refractions are the same within the experimental variation. This is because the larger specific volume of the uncharged isomer compensate for its lower refractive index in calculating the molar refraction by Equation 2. It can be concluded that electrostriction of water by an amino acid in solution increases its refractive index but has no effect on its molar refraction and that the molar refractions do not change significantly with temperature.

Table IV. Comparison of Molar Refractions of Amino Acids and Their Uncharged Isomer
(λ = 589 mμ)

Temp., °C.	Substance	Specific Volume[a], Cc.	Refractive Index	Molar Refraction, Cc.
5	Glycine		1.691	16.85
	Glycolamide		1.516	17.00
	Alanine		1.615	21.13
	Lactamide		1.496	21.47
25	Glycine	0.58	1.685	16.58
	Glycolamide	0.75	1.506	16.73
	Alanine	0.68	1.606	20.88
	Lactamide	0.83	1.490	20.99
40	Glycine		1.676	16.38
	Glycolamide		1.506	16.73
	Alanine		1.612	21.06
	Lactamide		1.489	21.21

[a] Specific volumes obtained at 25° also used to calculate refractive index values at 5° and 40°.

Effect of Ionization on the Refractive Index and Molar Refraction of Amino Acids and Proteins. Since the electrostriction produced by an amino acid does not affect its molar refraction, the ionization of an amino acid might be expected to produce no significant change in molar refraction. Table V indicates that this is the case, provided the large change in the volume of the amino acid as a result of ionization, found by Kauzmann, Bodanszky, and Rasper (23), is used in calculating molar refraction. The refractive index of an equivalent concentration of hy-

Table V. Effect of Ionization on the Refractive Index and Molar Refraction of Alanine and Ovalbumin
25° (λ = 589 mμ)

Substance	Refractive Index	Specific Volume, Cc.	Molar Refraction, Cc.
Alanine	1.615	0.682	21.1
Alanine$^+$ Cl$^-$	1.539	0.767	21.4
Alanine$^-$ Na$^+$	1.473	0.924	22.0
Ovalbumin			
pH 4.6	1.600	0.745	11,470
pH 3.8	1.598	0.747	11,475
pH 3.2	1.593	0.749	11,425
pH 2.5	1.592	0.753	11,466
pH 2.0	1.588	0.757	11,466

drochloric acid or sodium hydroxide was used instead of water in calculating molar refraction of the salts of alanine. Similarly, the data on the refractive index and molar refraction of ovalbumin in Table V indicate that acidification reduces the refractive index of ovalbumin; but if its volume changes, reported by Kauzmann, are taken into consideration, the molar refraction of ovalbumin does not change on acidification. This lack of change of molar refraction with charge may appear to be contrary to the findings of Perlmann and Longsworth (26) on the effect of charge on the refractive increment of proteins. However, this is not necessarily true, since they only calculated refractive increments. Their results do not take into consideration volume changes which take place with change in charge, reported by Kauzmann (22).

Specific Refractive Increments of Proteins. The specific refractive increments, $(n-n_0)c$, of a number of proteins have been determined by Armstrong et al. (2), Perlmann and Longsworth (26), Halwer, Nutting, and Brice (16), and Charlwood (7). These are of practical value in determining the concentration of protein solutions by means of the refractive index of the solution and have an accuracy of about ± 0.5%, as stated by Halwer, Nutting, and Brice (16). Consequently, values in Table VI are given to only three significant figures. In general, the

Table VI. Specific Refractive Increments of
Certain Proteins at 25°
$(n-n_0)c$, g/ml

Protein	Wavelength		
	589 mµ	546 mµ	436 mµ
Gelatin	0.184	0.186	0.191
α-Lactalbumin	0.188	0.189	0.195
β-Lactoglobulin	0.180	0.181	0.187
Lysozyme	0.184	-	-
Ovalbumin	0.178	0.181	0.185
Pepsin	0.177	0.182	0.188
Ribonuclease	0.185	0.186	0.192
Bovine serum albumin	0.183	0.188	0.193
Horse serum albumin	0.177	0.185	0.191
Human serum albumin	0.180	0.186	0.188

values listed in Table VI agree with those reported by Halwer, Nutting, and Brice (16) and Charlwood (7) for the same proteins.

Refractive Index of Proteins at Different Wavelengths. The refractive indices of amandin and heamocyanin were found by Putzeys and Brosteaux (27) to vary with the inverse square of the wavelength. A similar relation for the specific refractive increments of a number of proteins was reported by Perlmann and Longsworth (26). The refractive indices of several proteins are plotted as a function of the inverse square of wavelength for three wavelengths (mµ) in Figure 1. The slopes are essentially the same for the proteins listed and differ

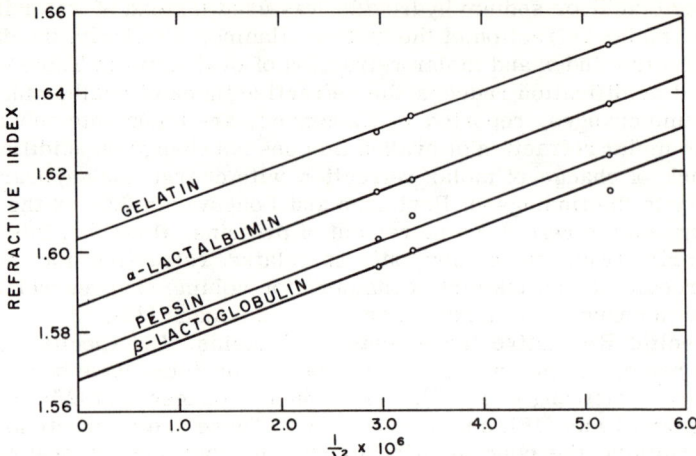

Figure 1. Variations in refractive index of proteins with wavelength in millimicrons, mµ

slightly from those reported by Putzeys and Brosteaux (27). The equation relating refractive index of the protein to wavelength is

$$n_p = B + (9.6 \times 10^3)/\lambda^2$$

where intercept B for gelatin, α-lactalbumin, pepsin, and β-lactoglobulin is 1.603, 1.586, 1.574, and 1.568, respectively.

Effect of Heat Denaturation on Refractive Index. Kauzmann (21) has pointed out that it should be possible to observe small changes in the index of refraction of a protein as a result of denaturation. In fact, he reported small changes in the refractive index of ovalbumin solutions denatured by urea, but, he found that these changes due to denaturation could be accounted for by accompanying changes in volume. Stauff and Rasper (29) also found small changes in the refractive index of chymotrypsinogen solutions on heating.

The effect of heat denaturation on the index of refraction of β-lactoglobulin solutions has been investigated. A 1% solution of β-lactoglobulin dissolved in phosphate buffer of pH 7 and 0.1 ionic strength (a half of which was sodium chloride) was denatured by heating at 80° for 150 minutes. These are the conditions used by Briggs and Hull (5) in their electrophoretic studies of the denaturation of β-lactoglobulin. The changes in refractive index due to denaturation were measured with the Brice-Halwer differential refractometer. An increase in the refractive index of a 1% solution of β-lactoglobulin was produced by heat denaturation, which amounted to a small but significant difference of 0.000017 in the refractive index between the heated and unheated solutions for the three wavelengths—436, 546, and 589 mµ.

Kauzmann (21) has stated that denaturation is accompanied by a contraction of several hundred cubic centimeters per 100,000 grams of protein. However, in the literature only urea denaturation is given. In the case of heat denaturation, no change in volume was found by Haurowitz (18), while Heymann (19) has reported an increase. We found no change in the specific volume of β-lactoglobulin due to heat denaturation; native β-lactoglobulin in veronal buffer, pH 8.5, and 0.1 ionic strength, had a specific volume of 0.755 and the denatured a value of 0.753.

Discussion

The essential agreement between the refractive indices of proteins calculated from their amino acid compositions and the experimentally determined values given in Table II is good evidence that the refractive index of protein solutions is largely determined by atomic refractory factors. This is in agreement with Tanford's (31) views concerning the fundamental factors determining the refractive index of protein solutions—that the refractive increment is a measure of local polarizability due to electron deformation and is little affected by long-range forces concerned in large molecules. However, the values calculated for the refractive indices of proteins tend to be slightly lower than the determined values. Thus, of ten proteins in Table II, eight give lower calculated than determined values for the refractive indices. This indicates that the spatial arrangement of the amino acid residues in a protein has a small effect on the refractive index of the protein, which is also indicated by the change in the refractive index of β-lactoglobulin on heat denaturation.

The small but significant increase in the refractive increment of heat-denatured β-lactoglobulin solutions is of the same order as found by Stauff and Rasper (29) for changes in the refractive index of heated chymotrypsin solutions. Kauzmann believes that this small change in refractive index can be accounted for by changes in volume. However, no change in specific volume of β-lactoglobulin solution due to denaturation could be detected by a method sensitive to changes in volume of the order of 0.3%. Consequently, it is felt that the small change in the refractive index of the β-lactoglobulin solution produced by heat denaturation is due to changes in polarizability rather than in volume.

Literature Cited

(1) Adair, G. S., Robinson, M. E., Biochem. J. 24, 993 (1930).
(2) Armstrong, S. H., Jr., Budka, M. J. E., Morrison, K. C., Hasson, M., J. Am. Chem. Soc. 69, 1747 (1947).
(3) Blumenfeld, O. O., Perlmann, G. E., J. Gen. Physiol. 42, 553 (1959).
(4) Brice, B. A., Halwer, M., J. Opt. Soc. Am. 41, 1033 (1951).
(5) Briggs, D. R., Hull, R., J. Am. Chem. Soc. 67, 2007 (1945).
(6) Buzzell, J. G., Tanford, C., J. Phys. Chem. 60, 1204 (1956).
(7) Charlwood, P. A., J. Am. Chem. Soc. 79, 776 (1957).
(8) Cohen, J. B., "Organic Chemistry," 5th ed., Part II, p. 28, Longmans Green, New York, 1928.
(9) Cohn, E. J., Edsall, J. T., in "Proteins, Amino Acids, and Peptides," pp. 370-375, Reinhold, New York, 1943.

(10) Craig, R., Schmidt, C. L. A., Australian J. Exptl. Biol. Med. Sci. 9, 33 (1932).
(11) Doty, P., Geiduschek, E. P., in "The Proteins," p. 1A, H. Neurath, K. Bailey, eds., Academic Press, New York, 1953.
(12) Fajans, K., in "Physical Methods of Organic Chemistry," 3rd ed., p. 1169, by A. Weissberger, Interscience, New York, 1960.
(13) Gordon, W. G., Basch, J. J., Kalan, E. B., J. Biol. Chem. 236, 2908 (1961).
(14) Gordon, W. G., Semmett, W. F., Cable, R. S., Morris, M., J. Am. Chem. Soc. 71, 3293 (1949).
(15) Gordon, W. G., Ziegler, J., Arch. Biochem. Biophys. 57, 80 (1955).
(16) Halwer, M., Nutting, G. C., Brice, B. A., J. Am. Chem. Soc. 73, 2786 (1951).
(17) Harrington, W. F., Schellman, J. A., Compt. Rend. Trav. Lab. Carlsberg, Ser Chim. 30, 21 (1956).
(18) Haurowitz, F., Kolloid Z. 71, 198 (1935).
(19) Heymann, E., Biochem. J. 30, 127 (1936).
(20) Hirs, C. H. W., Stein, W. H., Moore, S., J. Biol. Chem. 211, 941 (1954).
(21) Kauzmann, W., Advan. Protein Chemi. 14, 1 (1959).
(22) Kauzmann, W., Biochim. Biophys. Acta 28, 87 (1958).
(23) Kauzmann, W., Bodanszky, A., Rasper, J., J. Am. Chem. Soc. 84, 1777 (1962).
(24) McMeekin, T. L., Marshall, K., Science 116, 142 (1952).
(25) McMeekin, T. L., Wilensky, M., Groves, M. L. Biochem. Biophys. Res. Commun. 7, 151 (1962).
(26) Perlmann, G. E., Longsworth, L. G., J. Am. Chem. Soc. 70, 2719 (1948).
(27) Putzeys, P., Brosteaux, J., Bull. Soc. Chim. Biol. 18, 1681 (1936).
(28) Rothen, A., J. Gen. Physiol. 24, 203 (1940).
(29) Stauff, J., Rasper, J., Kolloid Z. 159, 97 (1958).
(30) Stein, W. H., Moore, S., J. Biol. Chem. 178, 79 (1949).
(31) Tanford, Charles, "Physical Chemistry of Macromolecules," Wiley, New York, 1961.
(32) Tilton, L. W., Taylor, J. K., J. Res. Natl. Bur. Std. 20, 419 (1938).
(33) Tristram, G. R., in "The Proteins," Vol. I, Part A, p. 221, H. Neurath, K. Bailey, eds., Academic Press, New York, 1953.

Received November 30, 1962. Reference to a company or product does not imply that the U. S. Department of Agriculture recommends it to the exclusion of others.

Conversion of Proline to Hydroxyproline in Collagen Synthesis

ALTON MEISTER, NEVILLE STONE, AND JAMES M. MANNING

*Department of Biochemistry,
Tufts University School of Medicine,
Boston, Mass.*

Granuloma minces from normal and ascorbate-deficient guinea pigs were incubated with labeled proline; collagen imino acids were subsequently isolated and their specific radioactivities determined. Although the specific activity of proline from scorbutic tissues was not markedly reduced, that of hydroxyproline was much lower than the controls. Use of proline-H^3 provided a new parameter for following hydroxylation, since H_2^3O formation paralleled that of hydroxyproline-H^3. There was a marked decrease of H_2^3O formation with ascorbate-deficient granuloma; addition of ascorbate increased H_2^3O and hydroxyproline-H^3 formation. The data suggest that collagen biosynthesis involves two proline pools; one supplies collagen proline. The other is oxidized to a hydroxyproline intermediate, not in equilibrium with free hydroxyproline nor in peptide linkage with proline. This hypothesis is considered in relation to currently available information about protein synthesis.

Collagen is the most abundant connective tissue protein and comprises as much as 30% of the total protein of some animals. As compared to other proteins, collagen is unusual in terms of its extracellular location, tertiary structure, amino acid composition, and apparently also the manner of its biosynthesis. Thus, it appears that collagen exists as a triple-stranded helix as first proposed by Ramachandran and Kartha (34) and later elaborated by others (1, 6, 7). Approximately two thirds of the amino acids of collagen may be accounted for by four amino acids: proline, 4-hydroxyproline, glycine, and glutamic acid. Collagen contains little or none of the sulfur-containing amino acids, very small amounts of tyrosine and phenylalanine, and no tryptophan. Collagen contains 5-hydroxylysine, and very recently evidence has been reported of the presence of small amounts of 3-hydroxyproline (28).

The biosynthesis of collagen differs from that of many other proteins in several major respects. For example, collagen exhibits a very low turnover and certain collagen fractions of animals remain with the animal for its lifetime (17, 49); yet, there is evidence of more labile forms of collagen and certain of these may be precursors of the mature insoluble collagen (17, 18). Free hydroxyproline is not incorporated to an appreciable extent into collagen. The early studies of Womack and Rose (53) showed that hydroxyproline did not replace arginine in supporting the growth of rats, although proline and glutamate, under the same dietary conditions, were effective. Stetten and Schoenheimer (45, 46), in experiments with N^{15}- and deuterium-labeled proline, showed that free proline rather than free hydroxyproline was the precursor of collagen hydroxyproline. In this work it was found that hydroxyproline was one twentieth as effective as proline as a precursor of collagen hydroxyproline. These studies, which have been confirmed by others (15, 26), have led to the suggestion (45) that hydroxylation of proline takes place in peptide linkage. Similar conclusions may apply to the 5-hydroxylysine of collagen; thus, lysine rather than hydroxylysine is the precursor of collagen hydroxylysine (31, 42).

Collagen synthesis takes place at a reduced rate in ascorbic acid deficiency (14, 38, 39, 52). For example, granulation tissue induced by wounding, or by introduction of a foreign substance such as polysaccharide or a polyvinyl sponge, contains much less collagen (and hydroxyproline) when such procedures are carried out in ascorbic acid-deficient guinea pigs. The function of ascorbic acid in collagen synthesis is not yet known. It has been suggested that it is required for the maintenance of collagen (16), for hydroxylation of peptide-bound proline, and for the maturation of fibroblasts (25); it might also function in a hormonally induced systemic effect. Studies by Gould (12) and Robertson and Hewitt (37), and in this laboratory (47, 48) suggest that this vitamin has a direct function in hydroxylation.

The present work was undertaken in an attempt to shed light on the mechanism of hydroxyproline formation in collagen biosynthesis and on the site of action of ascorbate. It was recognized that these phenomena were very likely to be closely interrelated. Proline labeled with tritium was used because it was anticipated that tritium released from proline during hydroxylation would appear in the tissue water as tritiated water. The use of tritiated proline in such a system might then provide a new parameter for following the hydroxylation reaction, provided that the formation of tritiated water was stoichiometrically related to the formation of hydroxyproline. Such an approach might conceivably permit the demonstration of hydroxylation and peptide bond formation as separate chemical steps.

Minces of collagen-forming granulomas were incubated with media containing C^{14}-labeled or tritiated proline (or other labeled amino acids). The tumors were induced in guinea pigs by injection of carrageenin as described by Robertson and Schwartz (39). Guinea pigs fed normal diets and ascorbate-deficient diets were employed. "Generally labeled" tritiated proline and tritiated proline obtained by tritiation of 3,4-dehydroproline (40) were used. The tritiated proline preparations were obtained from the New England Nuclear Corp., Schwarz Bioresearch, Inc., and Commissariat l'Énergie Atomique, Gif-sur-Yvette, France.

Collagen and the noncollagenous proteins were isolated by the general procedure indicated in Figure 1. The tissue was homogenized in

1. Tissue homogenized in 75% acetone
2. Homogenate centrifuged (1000 × g)
3. Residue washed in 95% ethanol (6×); ether-ethanol (3:1) (2×; 60°; 10 minutes); 95% ethanol
4. Collagen extracted from residue with 5% trichloroacetic acid (2×; 90°)

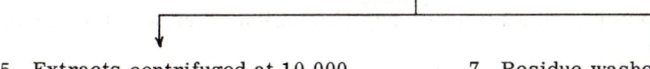

5. Extracts centrifuged at 10,000 × g; collagen precipitated by addition of tannic acid at 0°
6. Collagen-tannate washed with 5% tannic acid at 0°

7. Residue washed with 5% trichloroacetic acid and 95% ethanol
8. Residue dissolved in N NaOH; 60°; 10 minutes; reprecipitated by addition of HCl and trichloroacetic acid
9. Residue (noncollagenous protein) washed with 95% ethanol

Figure 1. Scheme for Extraction of Collagen

acetone, treated with other solvents, and then extracted with hot trichloroacetic acid. Finally, the collagen was precipitated by addition of tannic acid. The imino acids were obtained from acid hydrolyzates of the collagen by ion-exchange chromatography after destruction of the α-amino acids by treatment with nitrous acid (38). In some experiments the imino acids were obtained by paper chromatography and electrophoresis.

The collagen isolated from deficient and control granulomas exhibited approximately the same amino acid composition as that of purified commercial gelatin. The amino acid composition was examined both by two-dimensional paper chromatography and by gas-liquid chromatography (19). The ratio of proline to hydroxyproline was virtually identical for collagen extracted from normal and deficient granulomas (Table I). Further indication of the purity of the isolated collagen is the fact that collagen does not contain tryptophan. Thus, when C^{14}-tryptophan was incubated with minces of the granuloma, significant quantities of radioactivity were incorporated into the noncollagenous protein but

Table I. Mole Ratio of Proline to Hydroxyproline in Collagen Isolated from Granuloma of Normal and Scorbutic Guinea Pigs[a]

Source of Granuloma	Mole Ratio Proline/Hydroxyproline
Normal	1.24
Normal	1.28
Scorbutic	1.24
Scorbutic	1.26

[a] Collagen isolated from granuloma as tannate and hydrolyzed in 6N HCl; imino acids isolated as described in text, and quantitatively determined (27, 59).

not into the collagen (Table II). Water was obtained from the reaction mixtures by lyophilization. The radioactivity of the isolated imino acids and the trapped water was determined by counting with a Chicago Nuclear Co. dual-window scintillation counter. In some of the experiments with C^{14}-amino acids, an automatic gas flow mica window counter was employed.

In the experiments reported in Table III 2 grams of granuloma mince were incubated with 5 ml. of medium containing 5 μc. of "3,4-tritiated" (batch 64-121-1) L-proline (173 μc. per μmole) or 1 μc. of DL-proline-1-C^{14} (3.1 μc. per μmole) (obtained from the New England Nuclear Corp., Boston, Mass.). Incubation was carried out at 37° C. under 95% oxygen–5% carbon dioxide. The medium contained 0.022M NaCl, 0.003M KCl, 0.0012M $MgSO_4$, 0.0013M $CaCl_2$, 0.0004M KH_2PO_4, 0.025M $NaHCO_3$, and 0.01M D-glucose. Tritium and carbon-14 were determined by liquid scintillation counting. The deficient animals were deprived of ascorbic acid for 2 weeks. Proline and hydroxyproline were

Table II. Incorporation of C^{14}-Tryptophan into Collagen and Noncollagenous Proteins of Guinea Pig Granuloma

Expt. No.	Noncollagenous Protein, C.p.m./Mg.	Collagen Tannate, C.p.m./Mg. (Approx.)
1	108	2
2	94	3
3	17	1
4	40	1
5	27	0
6	69	1

[a] Reaction mixtures contained 7 × 10^4 c.p.m. of 3-C^{14}-DL-tryptophan (10 curies/mole); incubated for 4 hours; other conditions as in Table III. Noncollagenous proteins processed by method of Siekevitz (41).

Table III. Incorporation of Proline into Collagen Proline and Hydroxyproline of Granulomas from Normal and Scorbutic Guinea Pigs

			Specific Activity, D.P.M./μmole			
		Incubation	Normal		Deficient	
Isotope	Expt. No.	Period, Min.	Proline	Hydroxy-proline	Proline	Hydroxy-proline
H^3	1	30	6,150	2,400	4,580	< 100
		60	13,300	5,070	9,300	150
		120	21,300	8,700	17,800	360
C^{14}	2	30	790	695	787	< 10
C^{14}	3	30	745	680	530	70

isolated from acid hydrolyzates of the collagen by paper chromatography (solvent 1-butanol–acetic acid–water, 4:1:1) and determined, respectively, as described by Troll and Linnsley (50) and Neuman and Logan (27).

Results

As indicated in Figure 2, when minces of tumor obtained from normal and ascorbic acid–deficient animals were incubated with C^{14}-proline, much more radioactivity was incorporated into the collagen of the normal tissue. When the specific radioactivities of the isolated imino acids were examined (Table III), several conclusions were possible. In the experiments with granuloma from normal animals and C^{14}-proline, the values for hydroxyproline were not far from those of proline. With the scorbutic granulomas, the specific activity of the isolated proline was not greatly reduced, compared to that obtained from the normal granuloma. In contrast, the specific activity of the hydroxyproline isolated from the deficient tissues was markedly reduced. Similar results were obtained in the studies with tritiated proline. Thus, the specific activity of the proline isolated from the deficient granuloma was only moderately reduced, whereas the specific activity of the hydroxyproline was extremely low. This observation may be explained in terms of a dual-pathway mechanism of proline incorporation, considered below.

In contrast to the results obtained with C^{14}-proline, the hydroxyproline isolated from the normal granuloma in the experiments with tritiated proline exhibited a much lower specific activity than the proline isolated from the same source. These findings indicate that tritium was lost from proline during hydroxylation; determination of the tritium-C^{14} ratios for proline and hydroxyproline obtained from normal collagen (Table IV) indicates that approximately one half of the proline tritium was lost during hydroxylation. Results consistent with this conclusion are shown in Table V, which gives the total values for the radioactivities of the water and the collagen hydroxyproline. Thus, there was, within experimental error, as much isotope found in the water as in the collagen hydroxyproline.

Figure 3 shows the dramatic effect of ascorbic acid deprivation on

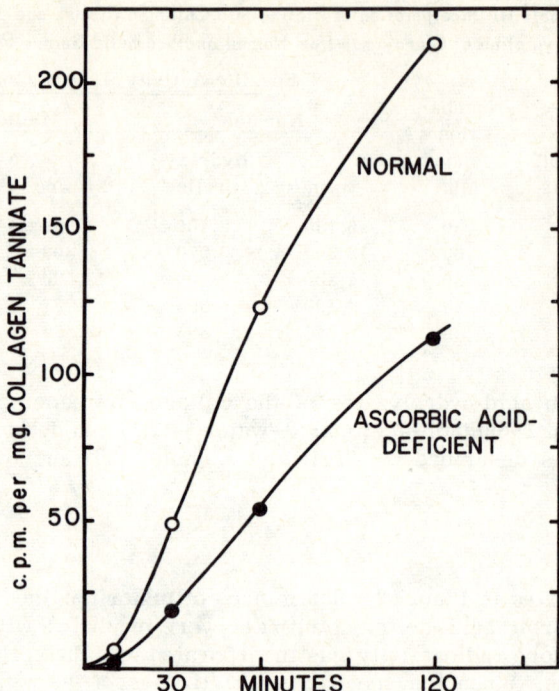

Figure 2. In vitro incorporation of C^{14}-proline into granuloma collagen

Experimental details as in Table III

tritiated water formation. The available data suggest that virtually all of the tritiated water formed is associated with hydroxylation of proline. In studies with both C^{14}-proline and tritiated proline we have not

Table IV. Ratios of Tritium to Carbon-14 for Proline and Hydroxyproline Isolated from Collagen[a]

Expt. No.	Incubation Time, Minutes	H^3/C^{14} Ratio		Ratio A/B
		A Hydroxyproline	B Proline	
1	30	3.45	7.80	0.44
	60	2.65	4.53	0.58
	120	2.72	4.78	0.57
2	30	2.98	4.80	0.62
	60	2.60	4.73	0.55
	120	2.60	4.62	0.56

[a] C^{14}-proline and H^3-proline used together; experimental conditions as in Table III.

Table V. Radioactivities of Tritiated Hydroxyproline and Tritiated Water after Incorporation of Tritiated Proline into Collagen

Expt. No.	State of Animal	Hydroxyproline, D.P.M.	H_2^3O, D.P.M.
1	Normal	62,000	61,000
2	Normal	46,300	53,000
3	Deficient	11,500	13,900
	+ 50 µg./ml. ascorbate	22,100	20,400
	+ 80 µg./ml. ascorbate	20,500	27,100

Experimental conditions as in Table III.

found the isotope in glutamate or other amino acids. Similar observations were made by Green and Lowther (15) with C^{14}-proline. It therefore appears that in this tumor metabolism of proline to products other than hydroxyproline is negligible. The very low level of tritiated water formation in the deficient tissues (Figure 3) is also consistent with the absence of significant alternative pathways of proline metabolism under these conditions.

The data given in Table VI show that there was a considerable increase in formation of tritiated water upon in vitro addition of ascorbic acid. Addition of ascorbic acid failed to increase tritiated water formation with minces of normal granuloma, and no effect was observed

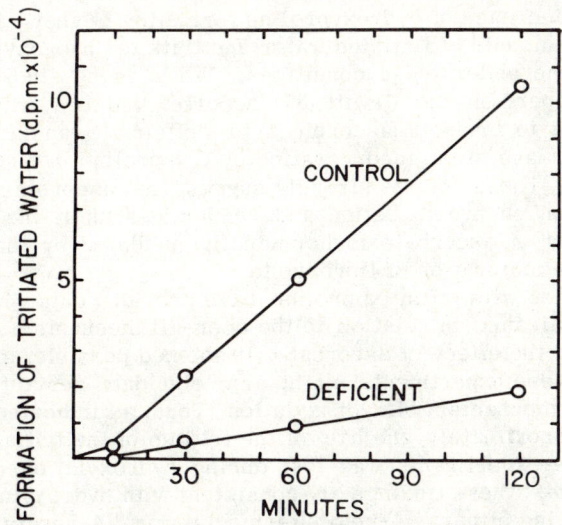

Figure 3. Formation of tritiated water from tritiated proline by granuloma from normal and scorbutic guinea pigs

Conditions as in Table III

Table VI. Stimulation of Hydroxylation of Proline by Ascorbic Acid-Deficient Granuloma by in Vitro Addition of Ascorbic Acid[a]

Expt. No.	Time	Ascorbate Added, μg./Ml.	Tritiated Water, D.P.M.
1	Deficient	None	19,700
		800	45,500
2	Deficient	None	14,400
		20	25,700
		100	23,100
3	Normal	None	27,200
		20	30,600
		100	26,500
4	Normal [b]	None	7,850
		100	8,050
		800	8,550
	Normal (boiled) [b]	None	880
		100	790
		800	790

[a] Experimental conditions as in Table III.
[b] 1 gram of mince and 1.3×10^6 d.p.m. of tritiated proline used; final volume, 2.5 ml.

with preparations that had been inactivated by boiling for 5 minutes prior to the experiment. That addition of ascorbic acid is associated also with an increase of hydroxyproline formation is shown in Table V; the relative amounts of tritiated water and tritiated hydroxyproline remain the same under these conditions. While these studies were in progress, Robertson and Hewitt (37) reported that in vitro addition of ascorbic acid to breis of ascorbic acid–deficient granulation tissues led to an increase in the incorporation of C^{14}-proline into collagen hydroxyproline. These results strongly suggest that ascorbic acid exerts a direct action on hydroxylation and render less likely the possibility that the effect of ascorbate is hormonally mediated or that it is required for the maturation of fibroblasts.

The studies with tritiated proline have provided data which appear to be of significance in relation to the over-all mechanism of collagen synthesis and the effect of ascorbate. It seemed possible, at least initially, that these experiments might also elucidate certain aspects of the chemical mechanism of hydroxylation. Thus, as indicated in Tables IV and V, approximately one half of the tritium of the tritiated proline used in these experiments was lost during hydroxylation. As stated previously (48), "these findings are consistent with hydroxylation mechanisms involving either a 4-keto intermediate or 3,4-unsaturation, assuming random distribution of tritium at proline carbons 3 and 4, and absence of significant isotope effects." Ebert and Prockop (8) incorrectly stated that Stone and Meister "observed a loss of both hydrogens from the carbon position on which hydroxylation occurs." Recent studies (9, 10, 33) indicate that the 4-oxygen atom of hydroxyproline in chick embryos arises from atmospheric oxygen rather than water. These findings suggest that an oxygenase mechanism is involved in the hydroxylation of proline, and render unlikely the formation of a 3,4-unsaturated intermediate which subsequently adds water.

Smith and Mitoma (43) have found an enzyme activity in mammalian tissues capable of reducing 4-keto-L-proline to L-hydroxyproline; such a reaction (perhaps involving bound forms of ketoproline or hydroxyproline) might conceivably function in hydroxyproline formation.

In an attempt to learn whether collagen hydroxyproline synthesized in granuloma minces incubated with tritiated proline contained tritium at the 4 position, we converted such tritiated hydroxyproline to the corresponding N-carbobenzoxy derivative and then oxidized this derivative with chromic acid to N-carbobenzoxy-4-ketoproline according to the procedure of Patchett and Witkop (29). In most of these experiments very little tritiated water was formed; although some tritiated water was detected in several experiments, the small amount formed could logically be attributed to adventitious oxidative reactions or perhaps to enolization of ketoproline. The evidence was therefore consistent with the absence of tritium at carbon atom 4 of the isolated hydroxyproline.

Any conclusions drawn from these experiments rest upon three assumptions: that the tritiated proline was labeled in the 3 and 4 positions only, that the label was randomly distributed in these positions, and that no significant isotope effects occurred.

Studies analogous to those described in Table V were carried out with two preparations of "generally labeled" tritiated prolines. The results (Table VII) indicate that two sevenths of the proline tritium was

Table VII. Radioactivities of Tritiated Water and Tritiated Hydroxyproline after Incorporation of Generally Tritiated Proline into Collagen

Expt. No.	Tritiated Water, D.P.M. (A)	Hydroxyproline, D.P.M. (B)	Ratio A/A + B
1[a]	8,350	20,100	0.29
2[a]	8,800	21,200	0.29
3[b]	139,000	334,000	0.29

[a] 2 grams of minced granuloma (from normal animal) and 5.0 µc. of generally labeled tritiated DL-proline (Comissariat l'energie Atomique; 44 curies/mole) used; incubation period, 2 hours.

[b] 15 µc. of generally labeled tritiated L-proline (Schwarz BioResearch, Inc.; 1000 curies/mole) used. Other conditions as in Table III.

liberated as tritiated water during hydroxylation. Although the results with the two different preparations of tritiated proline were the same, conclusions concerning the specific positions from which tritium is lost require assumptions similar to those given above.

The "generally labeled" proline preparation used in experiments 1 and 2 was converted to pyrrolid-2-one hydrochloride as described by Bragg and Hough (2). The specific activity of the proline was 5.7×10^8

c.p.m. per mole, and that of the product [(pyrrolid-2-one)$_2$HCl] was 1.06 × 10^9 c.p.m. per mole. The ratio of these values is 0.54; a ratio of 0.58 would be expected for uniformly tritiated proline.

That one or more of these assumptions may be open to question is suggested by the very recent studies of Ebert and Prockop (8) and by subsequent work in our laboratory with another batch (No. 73-253) of "3,4-tritiated" proline obtained from the New England Nuclear Corp. In experiments with this material, less tritium appeared in the water than in the studies described in Table V. Thus, under the conditions of the studies described in Table V, 96,800 d.p.m. of tritiated water and 186,000 d.p.m. of tritiated hydroxyproline were found. In experiments with both "uniformly labeled" C^{14}-proline and the new batch of "3,4-tritiated" proline, H^3/C^{14} ratios for hydroxyproline and proline were 1.79 and 2.56, respectively, leading to an A/B value (cf. Table IV) of 0.70.

Ebert and Prockop (8) carried out similar studies with "3,4-tritiated" proline in chick embryos, and reported ratios of 0.73 and 0.74. Information supplied by Prockop (32) indicates that this material was from a batch (New England Nuclear Corp.) different from those used by us. They converted the isolated hydroxyproline to pyrrole and found ratios of the H^3/C^{14} values for pyrrole to hydroxyproline of 0.61 and 0.64 (these values were corrected for loss of carboxyl C^{14}, assuming random labeling). We have recently converted the H^3-hydroxyproline obtained in our experiments with the new batch of "3,4-tritiated" proline to pyrrole (32), and obtained values of 0.70 and 0.73. However, conversion of this hydroxyproline to N-carbobenzoxy-4-ketoproline did not lead to a significant decrease in specific activity, suggesting that little tritium was present at carbon atom 4 of the isolated hydroxyproline.

It is evident that the studies with tritiated proline do not permit definite conclusions about the mechanism of hydroxylation; further information is needed about the labeling of the proline used and possible isotope effects. It is probable that there is some randomization of label during tritiation of 3,4-dehydroproline (40), and apparently also some racemization. Thus, we have observed that the tritiated proline preparations contain 10 to 20% D-proline and that oxidation by D-amino acid oxidase releases significant amounts of tritiated water.

Despite the divergent results obtained with different preparations of tritiated proline, we have found that the ratio of the tritiated water formed to the tritiated hydroxyproline formed is constant for a given batch of tritiated proline. Since in the carrageenin tumor system there is a definite relationship between the formation of tritiated water and tritiated hydroxyproline, this system should be of value in obtaining definitive results when appropriately labeled prolines are available. This is apparently not true for the chick embryo, in which there is a considerable metabolism of proline to other products and therefore a much greater formation of tritiated water (23).

In the original studies of Stetten and Schoenheimer (46) (who employed proline labeled with N^{15} and deuterium in positions 3, 4, and 5), N^{15} : D ratios of 0.18 and 0.13 were obtained for the isolated hydroxyproline and proline, respectively. The ratio of the value obtained for proline to that for hydroxyproline was therefore 0.72. A value of 0.83 would have been expected for the loss of one atom of deuterium, while 0.67 may be calculated for the loss of two atoms of deuterium. The result of Stetten and Schoenheimer therefore lies between these two calculated values, although closer to a value consistent with the loss of two atoms of deuterium.

Although we must tentatively put aside the question of the detailed chemical mechanism of hydroxylation, the present data appear to provide insight into the relationship between hydroxylation and collagen synthesis. Thus, we may first consider a mechanism as shown below, based on the suggestion of Stetten.

$$\text{Proline} \longrightarrow [(\text{pro})_{\underline{n}}\text{-peptide}] \longrightarrow [(\text{pro})_{\underline{n}-\underline{x}}\text{-}(\text{hypro})_{\underline{x}}\text{-peptide}] \longrightarrow \text{collagen}$$

According to such a scheme, proline is incorporated into collagen through a series of precursor peptides; ultimately about half of the proline residues of such peptides are converted to hydroxyproline. If this mechanism were correct, one would expect a proline-rich collagen precursor to accumulate in scurvy. However, satisfactory evidence for this type of intermediate has not yet been published. In addition, our data indicate identical proline-hydroxyproline ratios for collagen obtained from scorbutic and normal granulomas. According to this scheme, the ratio of the specific activity of collagen hydroxyproline to that of collagen proline should not exceed unity. However, ratios much greater than unity have been found by Green and Lowther (15), who have observed ratios as high as 1.69. We have made similar observations.

The striking fall in the specific activity of the collagen hydroxyproline isolated from deficient granulomas observed in the present study (Table III) suggests an alternative scheme of collagen synthesis.

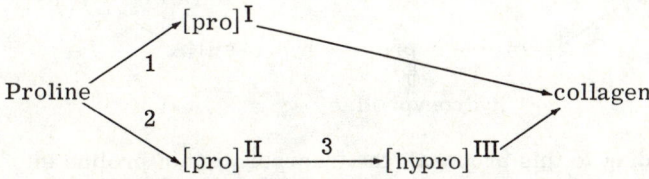

According to this proposal, proline is converted to collagen proline and collagen hydroxyproline by two separate and distinct pathways. Proline destined to become hydroxyproline is oxidized to a bound hydroxyproline intermediate, which does not equilibrate significantly with free hydroxyproline and is not yet in peptide linkage with proline. The marked drop in the specific activity of hydroxyproline in scorbutic collagen may then be explained by the accumulation of an intermediate or intermediates in the hydroxyproline pathway. Such accumulation would lead to a much greater dilution of the proline destined to become collagen hydroxyproline than proline which will become collagen proline. A block at either step 2 or step 3 in the scheme given here would be expected to lead to the observed decrease in formation of tritiated water. It appears unlikely that in scurvy there is a block between free proline and the first bound proline intermediate. Such a block would lead to proline accumulation and thus dilute proline for both pathways. Similar considerations indicate that intermediate I and intermediate II cannot be identical.

It is conceivable that the reduced formation of tritiated water observed in scurvy could be due to a general reduction in protein synthesis, but this would not explain the marked differences between the specific activities of proline and hydroxyproline observed, nor would it explain observations in our laboratory that glycine and tyrosine are incorporated at rates similar to that of incorporation of proline into the collagen of granuloma obtained from scorbutic animals.

The striking increases in the formation of tritiated water and tritiated hydroxyproline on in vitro addition of ascorbate are consistent with a function of this vitamin in hydroxylation—probably at step 3. The present results do not support a systemic ascorbic acid–mediated effect, the belief that ascorbic acid functions in the maintenance of collagen, or acts by stimulating maturation of the fibroblasts in the system under study here. The present data do not support the possibility that intermediates containing hydroxyproline accumulate in scurvy. The proposal that ascorbic acid is involved in the hydroxylation reaction itself is consistent with studies on the nonenzymatic hydroxylation of proline (4) and on enzymatic hydroxylation of other compounds (5, 20, 21, 44, 51).

A more elaborate and somewhat speculative scheme for the formation of collagen and the conversion of proline to collagen hydroxyproline is:

$$\begin{array}{c} \text{E-pro-AMP} \longrightarrow \text{pro-sRNA} \\ \nearrow \qquad\qquad\qquad\qquad \searrow \\ \text{Proline} \qquad\qquad\qquad\qquad\qquad\qquad \text{collagen} \\ \searrow \qquad\qquad\qquad\qquad \nearrow \\ [\text{pro}] \longrightarrow [\text{hypro}] \longrightarrow \text{hypro-sRNA} \\ \updownarrow \\ \text{hydroxyproline} \end{array}$$

According to this proposal, the incorporation of proline into collagen follows the acyl adenylate and acyl RNA stages now generally believed to occur in protein synthesis. A bound hydroxyproline intermediate is postulated, from which hydroxyproline is transferred to soluble RNA. We prefer to suggest that different RNA acceptor molecules exist for hydroxyproline and proline; this would be consistent with recent work which indicates that the soluble RNA molecule contains the information for incorporation of a particular amino acid into protein (3). Although it is conceivable that there is hydroxylation of prolyl-sRNA to yield hydroxyprolyl-sRNA, an additional mechanism would be needed to distinguish the two types of acyl ribonucleic acids. If the template recognizes only the soluble RNA and not the amino acid, hydroxylation must occur prior to acyl-RNA formation. If two types of prolyl-RNA exist (one of the precursor of collagen proline and the other that of collagen hydroxyproline), the hydroxylation system as well as the template must be able to distinguish between the two types of RNA molecules. According to the proposed scheme, one would predict a specific nucleotide sequence code for hydroxyproline (or the bound hydroxyproline intermediate).

There is evidence that free hydroxyproline can be incorporated into collagen to some extent. Thus, Mitoma (26) found that free hydroxyproline was incorporated into chick embryo collagen at about 10% of the rate observed with proline. The scheme given above indicates a pathway by which there may be a relatively slow influx of hydroxyproline into the hydroxyproline intermediate. Similarly, the breakdown of this intermediate might be responsible for the formation of free hydroxyproline observed in some tissues and possibly also that found in urine.

If this scheme is correct, it should be possible to obtain conditions under which protein synthesis but not hydroxylation is blocked. That this may be possible experimentally is suggested by the results of recent experiments (24) in our laboratory, which have shown that in the presence of puromycin, the formation of collagen hydroxyproline determined in carageenin tumors as described here is markedly reduced, but that hydroxylation (as determined by the formation of tritiated water and tritiated hydroxyproline) continues. Further work—especially efforts directed at isolation of intermediates—are in progress.

Manner and Gould (22) have reported that the formation of free hydroxyproline in chick embryos treated with puromycin continues in the absence of significant collagen formation. This finding is analogous to our observations on carrageenin tumors. Manner and Gould also obtained evidence for the formation of hydroxyprolyl-RNA in chick embryos, and concluded that proline can be converted to hydroxyproline without prior incorporation of proline into protein. On the other hand, Peterkofsky and Udenfriend concluded in a preliminary report (30) that a microsomal RNA-bound polypeptide of considerable size is the substrate for hydroxylation. The latter conclusion was based on studies with a cell-free chick embryo system in which puromycin and ribonuclease were added at various time intervals during the course of incubation with labeled proline. Manner and Gould (22) and Peterkofsky and Udenfriend (30) observed lag periods in the formation of hydroxyproline (compare Figures 2 and 3). Additional study on the nature of the intermediates involved in the incorporation of proline into the collagen imino acids is needed.

Conclusions

The present studies have shown that the in vitro carrageenin tumor system can be employed with tritiated proline to provide a procedure satisfactory for following hydroxylation by measurement of tritiated water. The data support a dual-pathway mechanism of proline incorporation and indicate that ascorbic acid functions at the hydroxylation step. These studies suggest specific experiments with cell-free systems in which intermediates containing proline and hydroxyproline, and subsequently, specific enzymes, may be isolated.

Literature Cited

(1) Bear, R. S., J. Biophys. Biochem. Cytol. 2, 363 (1956).
(2) Bragg, P. D., Hough, L., J. Chem. Soc. 814, 4050 (1958).
(3) Chapeville, F., Federation Proc. 21, 414 (1962).
(4) Chvapil, M., Hurych, J., Nature, 184, 1145 (1959).
(5) Cooper, J. R., Ann. N. Y. Acad. Sci. 92, 208 (1961).
(6) Cowan, P. M., McGavin, S., North, A.T.C., Nature 176, 1062 (1955).
(7) Crick, F. H. C., Rich, A., J. Mol. Biol. 3, 483 (1961).
(8) Ebert, P. S., Prockop, D. J., Biochem. Biophys. Res. Commun. 8, 305 (1962).
(9) Fujimoto, D., Osawa, H., Tamiya, H., Symp. Enz. Chem. (Fukuoka, Japan), Preliminary Issue, 14, 28 (1962).
(10) Fujimoto, D., Tamiya, H., Biochem. J. 84, 333 (1962).
(11) Gould, B. S., Ann. N. Y. Acad. Sci. 92, 168 (1961).
(12) Gould, B. S., J. Biol. Chem. 232, 637 (1958).
(13) Gould, B. S., Manner, G., Goldman, H. M., Stolman, J. M., Ann. N. Y. Acad. Sci. 85, 385 (1960).
(14) Gould, B. S., Woessner, J. F., J. Biol. Chem. 226, 289 (1957).
(15) Green, N. M., Lowther, D. A., Biochem. J. 71, 55 (1959).
(16) Gross, J., J. Exptl. Med. 109, 557 (1959).
(17) Harkness, R. D., Marko, A. M., Muir, H. N., Neuberger, A., Biochem. J. 56, 558 (1954).
(18) Jackson, D. S., "Symposium on Connective Tissue," p. 62, Blackwell, London, 1958.
(19) Johnson, D. E., Scott, S., Meister, A., Anal. Chem. 33, 669 (1961).
(20) LaDu, B. N., Zannoni, V. G., Ann. N. Y. Acad. Sci. 92, 175 (1961).
(21) Lindstedt, G., Lindstedt, S., Biochem. Biophys. Res. Commun. 7, 394 (1962).
(22) Manner, G., Gould, B. S., Biochim. Biophys. Acta 72, 243 (1963).
(23) Manning, J. M., unpublished results.
(24) Manning, J. M., Stone, N., Meister, A., unpublished data.
(25) Mitoma, C., Smith, T. E., J. Biol. Chem. 235, 426 (1959).
(26) Mitoma, C., Smith, T. E., Friedberg, F., Rasford, C., Ibid., 234, 78 (1959).
(27) Neuman, R. E., Logan, M. A., Ibid., 148, 299 (1950).
(28) Ogle, J. D., Logan, M. A., Arlinghaus, R. B., Federation Proc., 20, 1e (1961); J. Biol. Chem. 237, 3667 (1962).
(29) Patchett, A. A., Witkop, B., J. Am. Chem. Soc. 79, 189 (1957).
(30) Peterkofsky, B., Udenfriend, S., Biochem. Biophys. Res. Commun. 12, 257 (1963).
(31) Piez, K. A., Likins, R. C., J. Biol. Chem. 229, 101 (1957).
(32) Prockop, D., personal communication.
(33) Prockop, D., Kaplan, A., Udenfriend, S., Biochem. Biophys. Res. Commun. 9, 162 (1962).
(34) Ramachandran, G. N., Kartha, G., Nature 176, 593 (1955).
(35) Robertson, W. van B., Ann. N. Y. Acad. Sci. 92, 159 (1961).
(36) Robertson, W. van B., J. Biol. Chem. 196, 403 (1952).
(37) Robertson, W. van B., Hewitt, J., Biochim. Biophys. Acta 49, 404 (1961).

(38) Robertson, W. van B., Hewitt, J., Herman, C., J. Biol. Chem. 234, 105 (1959).
(39) Robertson, W. van B., Schwarz, B., Ibid., 201, 689 (1953).
(40) Robertson, A. V., Witkop, B., J. Am. Chem. Soc. 84, 1697 (1962).
(41) Siekevitz, P., J. Biol. Chem. 195, 549 (1952).
(42) Sinex, F. M., Van Slyke, D. D., Christman, D. R., Ibid., 234, 918 (1959).
(43) Smith, T. E., Mitoma, C., Ibid., 237, 1177 (1962).
(44) Staudinger, Hj., Krisch, K., Leonhäuser, S., Ann. N. Y. Acad. Sci. 92, 195 (1961).
(45) Stetten, M. R., J. Biol. Chem. 181, 31 (1949).
(46) Stetten, M. R., Schoenheimer, R., Ibid., 153, 113 (1944).
(47) Stone, N., Meister, A., Federation Proc. 21, 414 (1962).
(48) Stone, N., Meister, A., Nature 194, 555 (1962).
(49) Thompson, R. C., Ballou, J. E., J. Biol. Chem. 223, 795 (1956).
(50) Troll, W., Lindsley, J., Ibid., 215, 655 (1955).
(51) Udenfriend, S., Clark, C. T., Axelrod, J., Brodie, B. B., Ibid., 208, 731, 741 (1954).
(52) Wolbach, S. B., Howe, P. R., Arch. Pathol. Lab. Med. 1, 1 (1926).
(53) Womack, W., Rose, W. C., J. Biol. Chem. 171, 37 (1947).

Received December 14, 1962. Taken in part from a dissertation submitted by Neville Stone in partial fulfillment of the requirements for the degree of doctor of philosophy, Department of Biochemistry, Tufts University School of Medicine, 1962. Work supported by the National Institutes of Health, Public Health Service, and the National Science Foundation.

6

The Administration of Radioactive L-Cystathionine to a Human Cystinuric

VINCENT du VIGNEAUD, JULIAN R. RACHELE, JOHN E. WILSON,
FRED PLUM, AND LESTER J. REED

*Department of Biochemistry, and Department of Medicine,
Cornell University Medical College, and New York Hospital,
New York 21, N. Y.*

The present communication is concerned with experimental work carried out some years ago, in which cystathionine labeled with radioactive sulfur was administered to a human cystinuric (4). In 1936, Brand, Block, Kassell, and Cahill (3) advanced the hypothesis that carboxyaminopropyl-S–cysteine [later called cystathionine (2)] might be an intermediate in the formation of cysteine from methionine in the body. The synthesis of L-cystathionine (5) made it possible to subject this interesting hypothesis to experimental test. It was first demonstrated that cystathionine may be used in lieu of dietary cystine for the growth of rats (5) and subsequently that slices and extracts of rat liver are capable of cleaving cystathionine to cysteine (5). Tracer experiments then demonstrated that the sulfur of cystathionine may be utilized for cystine synthesis by the rat (10). In the present report direct evidence is offered that L-cystathionine serves as a source of sulfur for cystine synthesis in a human cystinuric.

Procedure

Radioactive L-cystathionine (10) (765 mg.) containing 6.85×10^6 counts per minute of S^{35} was fed to the human cystinuric patient who had served previously as the subject in an experiment demonstrating the formation of cystine from sulfur-labeled methionine (11). The same precautions were followed with regard to human experimentation involving radioactive material as in the latter experiment. After the feeding of the cystathionine, 24-hour urine specimens were collected for 3 days and sulfur distributions were determined by the titrimetric method of Fiske (6). Cystine determinations were carried out by the procedure of Sullivan, Hess, and Howard (12).

Cystine was recovered from aliquots of the urine samples, following the addition of carrier cystine by the procedure described previously (1̄1), and after recrystallization the isolated cystine samples gave satisfactory sulfur analysis.

Table I. Radioactivity Partition of Sulfur in the Urine of a Human Cystinuric[a]

765 mg. of L-cystathionine containing 6.85×10^6 c.p.m. of S^{35} administered at beginning of day 1

Urinary Sulfur Fraction	Sulfur Content, Mg.			Radioactivity, C.P.M. per Mg. S			Percentage of Total Administered Radioactivity		
	Day 1	Day 2	Day 3	Day 1	Day 2	Day 3	Day 1	Day 2	Day 3
Total sulfur	327	468	490	1522	4022	41	7.3	27.5	0.29
Total sulfate	163	309	277	1535	5460	23	3.7	24.7	0.09
Inorg. sulfate	149	259	234	1527	6196	23	3.3	23.4	0.08
Neutral sulfur	164	159	213	1511	1227	64	3.6	2.9	0.20
Cystine sulfur	35	92	64	331	95	2	0.17	0.13	0.002

[a] Radioactivity of sulfur of administered cystathionine and of urinary sulfur fractions determined in benzidine sulfate derived therefrom with use of a thin mica end window Geiger-Müller counter.

Radioactivity measurements were made upon benzidine sulfate recovered from the sulfur distribution determinations, as well as on benzidine sulfate from the sulfur analysis of the cystine samples. The results of these measurements are given in Table I.

Radioactive Sulfur in Urine

During the two days following the ingestion of the labeled cystathionine, approximately 35% of the administered radioactive sulfur appeared in the urine, compared to 16% during the two-day period following the ingestion of methionine by the same patient (11). On the other hand, 0.3% of the cystathionine sulfur appeared in urinary cystine, in contrast to 1.4% of the methionine sulfur. The conversion to urinary neutral sulfur compounds in the earlier experiment appeared to be much more rapid in its course than in the present experiment. While the oxidation of methionine sulfur to total sulfate had progressed at a fairly level rate, in the present study during the second day a very rapid rise in the oxidation of cystathionine sulfur to total sulfate occurred. Appreciable radioactivity was present also in cystine isolated from a hydrolyzate of a sample of hair, clipped on the 18th day of this experiment.

Our findings in this study are in harmony with the concept that L-cystathionine is an intermediate in the formation of cystine from methionine in man. Direct evidence for the existence of cystathionine in man was provided by the demonstration by Tallan, Moore, and Stein (13) of the occurrence of L-cystathionine in extracts of human brain. Moreover, cases of human cystathioninuria have been reported by Harris, Penrose, and Thomas (9) and by Frimpter, Haymovitz, and Horwith (8). The latter authors have also stated that an increased renal clearance of cystathionine is not observed in cystinuria. It is of considerable interest, however, that the mixed disulfide of L-cysteine and L-homocysteine was found by Frimpter (7) in the urines of all human cystinurics he had examined specifically for this unusual amino acid. In our own study, had the mixed disulfide existed in the urine of our patient, it would have been cleaved during the cuprous mercaptide isolation, its cysteine moiety becoming part of the finally isolated cystine.

Literature Cited

(1) Binkley, F., Anslow, W. P., Jr., du Vigneaud, V., J. Biol. Chem. **143**, 559 (1942).
(2) Binkley, F., du Vigneaud, V., Ibid., **144**, 507 (1942).
(3) Brand, E., Block, R. J., Kassell, B., Cahill, G. F., Proc. Soc. Exptl. Biol. Med. **35**, 501 (1936).
(4) du Vigneaud, V., "A Trail of Research in Sulfur Chemistry and Metabolism," p. 53, Cornell University Press, Ithaca, N. Y., 1952.
(5) du Vigneaud, V., Brown, G. B., Chandler, J. P., J. Biol. Chem. **143**, 59 (1942).
(6) Fiske, C. H., Ibid., **47**, 59 (1921).
(7) Frimpter, G. W., Ibid., **236**, PC51 (1961).
(8) Frimpter, G. W., Haymovitz, A. Horwith, M., New Eng. J. Med. **268**, 333 (1963).
(9) Harris, H., Penrose, L. S., Thomas, D. H. H., Ann. Human Genet. **23**, 442 (1959).
(10) Rachele, J. R., Reed, L. J., Kidwai, A. R., Ferger, M. F., du Vigneaud, V., J. Biol. Chem. **185**, 817 (1950).
(11) Reed, L. J., Cavallini, D., Plum. F., Rachele, J. R., du Vigneaud, V., Ibid., **180**, 783 (1949).
(12) Sullivan, M. X., Hess, W. C., Howard, H. W., Ibid., **145**, 621 (1942).
(13) Tallan, H. H., Moore, S., Stein, W. H., Ibid., **230**, 707 (1958).

Received October 7, 1963

7
Methionine Sulfoxide and Other Combined Amino Acids in the German Cockroach

S. MARK HENRY, RICHARD J. BLOCK, AND THOMAS W. COOK

*Boyce Thompson Institute for Plant Research, Inc.,
1086 North Broadway, Yonkers, N. Y.*

Alkaline hydrolysis of cockroach residues subsequent to extraction under nitrogen with 80% ethanol yielded methionine and methionine sulfoxide in a ratio of 10 to 1. Additional evidence for the presence of combined methionine sulfoxide was obtained by measuring the amount of methionine sulfoxide-S^{35} in acid and enzymatic hydrolyzates after assimilation of $Na_2S^{35}O_4$. The data are believed to be indicative of naturally occurring peptide- or polysaccharide-bound methionine sulfoxide. Other combined amino acids were determined by ion exchange chromatography of the 5% trichloroacetic acid–insoluble cockroach residues after hydrolysis with acid or alkali. β-Alanine, normally present only in the soluble fraction of an organism, was found in the insoluble, proteinaceous residue.

Methionine sulfoxide, $CH_3 \cdot SO \cdot CH_2CH(NH_2) \cdot COOH$, is reported by Dent[2] to be of rare occurrence in biological fluids. However, Dent (2, 3) states that methionine, $CH_3 \cdot S \cdot CH_2CH(NH_2) \cdot COOH$, is easily oxidized to the sulfoxide, particularly on paper chromatograms during development with phenol. Indeed, it appears that whenever methionine sulfoxide is detected, methionine should be suspected as the native form.

Reports of the presence of methionine sulfoxide are less frequent with respect to protein hydrolyzates than to free amino acid extracts. This is at least partially due to the fact that reduction and other changes occur upon hydrolysis with hydrochloric acid (16). The extent of decomposition depends on the conditions of hydrolysis and may approach 100%. One occasionally finds a published report of an amino acid analysis of protein in which data for methionine sulfoxide but not methionine are given. This is usually due to inadvertent treatment of the hydrolyzate in such a way as to cause oxidation of the normally occurring form of the amino acid.

Only a small number of proteins and peptides have been analyzed by various investigators by methods designed specifically to determine whether methionine sulfoxide is one of the constituent amino acids. One of these, an analog of the α-melanocyte–stimulating hormone from bovine pituitary glands (9), was found to contain the sulfoxide. However, the authors expressed some concern over the possibility of oxidation during isolation of the sample.

The present investigation was undertaken to determine if the methionine sulfoxide found by several investigators in insect tissue is a normal constituent of the amino acid pool and of protein. The amino acid composition of cockroach protein was simultaneously determined both qualitatively and quantitatively, since such data are available for few species of insects.

Experimental

Labeled methionine and methionine sulfoxide were detected radiometrically after assimilation of $Na_2S^{35}O_4$ by cockroaches. The conversion of inorganic sulfur to methionine was shown previously (5) to be due to intracellular symbiotic bacteria in these insects. In addition to this technique, unlabeled compounds were separated by column chromatography and measured colorimetrically.

Labeling of Sulfur Compounds in Tissue with S^{35}. The German cockroach, Blattella germanica (L.), selected for this study because of the large amounts of free methionine sulfoxide observed in previous investigations (5), was reared on a fortified dog biscuit diet (5) at 24° C. Full-grown nymphs were used without attempting to separate the sexes.

An aqueous solution of $Na_2S^{35}O_4$ was injected into the hemocele of 20 cockroaches by means of a micrometer-controlled hypodermic syringe fitted with a 30-gage steel needle. The insects were subsequently incubated at 25° C. for 2 days prior to being sacrificed.

Extraction Procedures. Ethanol Extraction. Ten of the S^{35}-injected insects were homogenized in about 5 ml. of hot 80% (v./v.) ethanol with a TenBroeck tissue grinder. The homogenate was centrifuged and, after decanting the supernatant fluid, the insoluble residue was washed three times with 80% ethanol. The supernatant liquids were combined and dried in vacuo. To prevent autoxidation of methionine, as much of the procedure as possible was conducted in an inert (nitrogen) atmosphere using nitrogen-saturated solvents.

Trichloroacetic Acid Extraction. The remaining 10 insects injected with $Na_2S^{35}O_4$ were homogenized in 5% (w./v.) trichloroacetic acid and the homogenate was kept at 100°C. in a water bath for 30 minutes. The homogenate was centrifuged, and the residue was washed once with 5 ml. of 5% trichloroacetic acid and then with distilled water. These fractions were added to the original supernatant solution and the combined mixture was dried in vacuo. The proteinaceous residue was then washed three times with a total of about 25 ml. of acidified ethanol (2 drops of 6N HCl per 50 ml. of ethanol) and three times with a similar quantity of ether. All solvents were saturated with nitrogen to minimize oxidation.

Trichloroacetic acid extraction was also the method of choice in preparing nonradioactive protein for analysis by column chromatography. Typically, 20 male and 20 female adult German cockroaches were maintained on a 3% (w./v.) glucose diet for 3 to 5 days. They were then homogenized in 20 ml. of 5% (w./v.) trichloroacetic acid. The homogenate was placed in a boiling water bath for 30 minutes, after which it was centrifuged. The insoluble material was washed once with each of the following solvents: water, hot acetone, and ethanol-benzene (5 to 95, v./v.), and twice with acidified ethanol followed by ethyl ether. The residue was then dried either under a stream of nitrogen or in a vacuum desiccator. In both sexes the dry residue comprised about 17% of the live weight of the insect.

For quantitative determinations of bound methionine sulfoxide and tryptophan, 10 cockroaches of each sex were homogenized and were extracted with the above solvents saturated with nitrogen.

Preparation of Extracts for Chromatography. The dried ethanolic extract was dissolved in 2 ml. of 10% (v./v.) 2-propanol, shaken with an equal volume of chloroform, and centrifuged. The chloroform layer was discarded. The trichloroacetic acid extract was taken up in 2 ml. of water and extracted four times with an equal volume of ether to remove trichloroacetic acid and lipides. The ether extract was discarded.

Hydrolysis of Protein. The radioactive, proteinaceous residues from the sulfate-injected insects were separated into equal fractions, one of which was hydrolyzed with acid and the other with proteolytic enzyme. Analyses of unlabeled protein were made after acid or alkaline hydrolysis.

Acid Hydrolysis. Twenty-five milliliters of 6N hydrochloric acid was added to 250 mg. of dry sample and the suspension was refluxed for 16 hours. The excess hydrochloric acid was removed by evaporation on a steam bath or on a rotary vacuum evaporator. The amino acids were then dissolved in 20 ml. of 10% 2-propanol. Samples so prepared were used directly for analysis by paper chromatography. Those samples to be analyzed by ion exchange chromatography were decolorized with a small amount of charcoal (Darco G-60) and filtered through paper. A 2-ml. aliquot of the filtrate was dried and redissolved in sodium citrate buffer at the pH and molarity required for application to the resin.

Alkaline Hydrolysis. Protein samples to be analyzed for tryptophan or methionine sulfoxide were hydrolyzed with barium hydroxide (16). Fifty milligrams of protein was the usual quantity hydrolyzed. After barium had been removed from the hydrolyzate (16), the pH of the solution was adjusted to 2.2 and the final volume to 22.5 ml. The entire procedure was conducted under nitrogen to minimize oxidation.

Enzymatic Hydrolysis. One-half of the S^{35}-labeled proteinaceous residue was suspended in 95 ml. of distilled water and the pH was adjusted to about 7.5 with 2N ammonium hydroxide. Five milliliters of ethanol and 10 mg. of Streptomyces griseus protease (Pronase,[1] 6 PU per gram) were added and the digestion mixture was incubated at 40°C. (13). After 3 days, the insoluble material was removed by filtration and the filtrate was dried in vacuo and redissolved in 2 ml. of 10% 2-propanol for chromatography. As in the above procedures, nitrogen-saturated solvents and nitrogenous atmospheres were used whenever possible in preparing the hydrolyzates.

Methionine-S^{35} Control Experiment. To determine what percentage of the methionine sulfoxide found in hydrolyzates and extracts is formed as a result of degradation of methionine during preparation and chromatography of the samples, the following experiment was conducted.

Ten anesthetized cockroaches were placed in the tissue grinder, to which was added 100 μl. of a solution of methionine-S^{35} (1400 counts per minute per microliter). The insects were homogenized with hot 80% ethanol and extracted at the same time and in the same way as the insects injected with sulfate. Another 10 insects were extracted with 5% trichloroacetic acid to which methionine-S^{35} had been added.

The proteinaceous residues were separated into equal aliquots and methionine-S^{35} was added to each. One aliquot from each type of extraction was hydrolyzed with acid and the other with proteolytic enzyme as described above. This control experiment was conducted simultaneously with the sulfate-injection experiment and under the same conditions.

Methionine Sulfoxide Adsorption Check. S^{35}-labeled methionine sulfoxide was prepared by oxidizing methionine-S^{35} with peroxide (6). Five microliters (ca. 20,000 counts per minute per microliter) of an aqueous solution of the sulfoxide was injected into each of 20 cockroaches. The first 10 were immediately immersed in hot 80% ethanol, and the remainder in hot 5% trichloroacetic acid to be homogenized and extracted. The extraction procedures were similar to those described above, except that precautions to prevent oxidation were not taken and the supernatant liquids, except for the acidified ethanol and ether washes, were not combined but were collected separately in 100-ml. volumetric flasks. The protein residues were hydrolyzed in 6N HCl and, like the other fractions, were then diluted to 100 ml. with water for radiometric analysis.

Paper Chromatography and Radiometry. For chromatography on paper 46 × 57 cm. sheets of Whatman No. 3 filter paper were used. Ten microliters of hydrolyzate or 30 μl. of extract was applied and the chromatograms were developed in the following systems.

System 1. The chromatograms were developed in the first direction with 60 parts of ethanol, 20 parts of tert-butyl alcohol, 5 parts of 58% (w./v.) NH_4OH, and 15 parts of H_2O, and in the second direction with 14 parts of tert-butyl alcohol, 3 parts of 88% (w./v.) formic acid, and 3 parts of H_2O (10).

System 2. The chromatograms were developed in the first direction with 450 parts of n-butyl alcohol, 50 parts of glacial acetic acid, and 125 parts of H_2O, and in the second direction with 2 parts of n-butyl alcohol, 2 parts of methyl ethyl ketone, and 1 part of H_2O. A shallow dish, containing 4N NH_4OH to replace the cyclohexylamine used by Mizell and Simpson (11), was placed in the chromatographic chamber for development in the second direction.

In order to maintain uniform conditions, all hydrolyzates or extracts were chromatographed simultaneously in the same chamber. A chromatogram of a standard amino acid mixture was used to locate the positions of methionine, methionine sulfoxide, and a second methionine sulfoxide spot formed as a result of oxidation of methionine during drying of the solvent used in the first direction.

Radioactivity was measured on the chromatograms with an end-window counting tube (4) following visualization of the amino acids with ninhydrin. The extracts and hydrolyzates from the methionine sulfoxide adsorption test were diluted to 100 ml. with water and 1-ml. aliquots were transferred to sample pans and dried for the estimation of radioactivity.

Column Chromatography. Amino acids were determined in hydrochloric acid hydrolyzates with a 150-cm. column of Amberlite IR-120 (17) using the Technicon AutoAnalyzer. Quantitative measurements were made colorimetrically (17). An alternate method of analysis made use of a 133-cm. column of Technicon chromobead resin and a modification of the sulfur system described by Piez and Morris (14). Although this method gave excellent separation of all classes of amino acids, its value was limited by the failure to separate cystine from glucosamine. Cystine values, therefore, were determined from the IR-120 chromatograms alone.

Although lysine, histidine, and arginine were separated on the chromobead resin, these and tryptophan were analyzed routinely on a 15-cm. column of Amberlite IR-120 (17) since a complete record of the basic amino acids could be obtained in less than 3 hours by this method.

Results

Soluble Methionine Sulfoxide. The percentages of soluble methionine sulfoxide-S^{35} found on chromatograms of cockroaches injected 2 days previously with $Na_2S^{35}O_4$ are given in Table I. Corresponding percentages from the control insects extracted in the presence of exogenous methionine-S^{35} are given in the same table. The amount of oxidation (up to 50%) occurring in the control is somewhat surprising. That this is not entirely due to oxidation during chromatography is indicated by the low levels of methionine sulfoxide found on paper chromatograms of the methionine-S^{35} solution used for the control experiment. Most of the free, labeled sulfoxide in the sulfate-injected insects is, therefore, due to spontaneous, nonenzymatic oxidation resulting from interaction with other components of the extract, probably during isolation or chromatography. The most likely time of occurrence is when the sample is drying after being applied to the paper. However, the percentage in the sulfate-injected insects is considerably higher than in the control insects. While the amount of oxidation may be influenced slightly by the addition of a small amount of methionine (control) it is believed that the difference represents actual sulfoxide in the 80% ethanol- and 5% trichloroacetic acid-extractable fraction of the cockroach.

Peptide-Bound Methionine Sulfoxide. The percentages of methio-

Table I. Methionine Sulfoxide-S^{35} in Soluble Fraction of Cockroaches Extracted by Two Methods and Chromatographed in Two Solvent Systems

Chromatographic Solvents[a]	Extraction Method	Methionine Sulfoxide-S^{35} as % of Total Reduced and Oxidized Methionine-S^{35} on Chromatogram[b]	Immediate Source of S^{35} in Amino Acids
System 1	Ethanol 80%	61	Injected $Na_2S^{35}O_4$
		43	Methionine-S^{35} added to homogenate
	Trichloroacetic acid 5%	66	Injected $Na_2S^{35}O_4$
		50	Methionine-S^{35} added to homogenate
System 2	Ethanol 80%	67	Injected $Na_2S^{35}O_4$
		40	Methionine-S^{35} added to homogenate
	Trichloroacetic acid 5%	74	Injected $Na_2S^{35}O_4$
		—	Methionine-S^{35} added to homogenate

[a] Solvent systems described in text.
[b] Methionine sulfoxide-S^{35} in solution used for control was found to be 7-10% of total S^{35} measured on chromatograms of aliquot of solution.

nine sulfoxide found on chromatograms of cockroach hydrolyzates (Table II) in these experiments are much lower than in the free amino acid fractions (Table I). Although these differences are due partially to variations in the chromatographic procedure, the very low percentages in the acid hydrolyzates indicate the involvement of other factors. For example, besides reduction of methionine sulfoxide during refluxing with hydrochloric acid, spontaneous sulfoxide formation from methionine appears to be inhibited in the presence of the small amounts of hydrochloric acid remaining in the sample after evaporation of the excess acid used for hydrolysis. It is also noted that a single aliquot of hydrolyzate was applied to the paper as compared with three applications of the 80% ethanol or 5% trichloroacetic acid extract. The additional drying required with three applications is undoubtedly responsible for greater oxidation.

More important than these possible differences in the methionine sulfoxide content of the extractable fraction and the protein are the differences in bound sulfoxide between the control and the sulfate-injected insects. Regardless of the method of extraction or of hydrolysis, the amount of bound methionine sulfoxide-S^{35} in the sulfate-injected insects is higher than that formed as a result of oxidation during hydrolysis and chromatography of the protein (control). As in the soluble fractions, these differences may be partially a reflection of a reduction-oxidation shift actuated by the presence of exogenous methionine in the control. Inspection of the data shows, in addition, that the percentage

Table II. Methionine Sulfoxide-S^{35} in Hydrolyzates of Proteinaceous Material Remaining after Extraction by Two Methods

Chromatographic Solvents [a]	Extraction Method	Methionine Sulfoxide-S^{35} as % of Total Reduced and Oxidized Methionine-S^{35} on Chromatogram		Immediate Source of S^{35} in Amino Acids
		Acid hydrolyzate	Enzyme hydrolyzate	
System 1	Ethanol 80%	14	16	Injected $Na_2S^{35}O_4$
		6	11	Methionine-S^{35} added to homogenate
	Trichloroacetic acid 5%	10	23	Injected $Na_2S^{35}O_4$
		4	12	Methionine-S^{35} added to homogenate
System 2	Ethanol 80%	11	26	Injected $Na_2S^{35}O_4$
		3	12	Methionine-S^{35} added to homogenate
	Trichloroacetic acid 5%	—	23	Injected $Na_2S^{35}O_4$
		4	17	Methionine-S^{35} added to homogenate

[a] Solvent systems described in text.

of methionine sulfoxide-S^{35} found on chromatograms of acid hydrolyzates is always lower than on those of enzyme-digested protein. This is due to reduction of the sulfoxide during hydrolysis (16) with acid.

Alkaline hydrolysis of protein from a mixed population of male and female cockroaches was found, by ion exchange chromatography, to yield a sample containing methionine and methionine sulfoxide in a ratio of 10 to 1. To determine whether any of this sulfoxide was formed as a result of the analytical procedure, another sample of the protein was hydrolyzed simultaneously with a sample of methionine alone and a sample of cockroach protein with added methionine. All three samples were treated in an identical manner, care being taken to prevent oxidation. The hydrolyzates, after removal of barium, were chromatographed on the 150-cm. column.

Table III. Methionine and Methionine Sulfoxide in Alkaline Hydrolyzates

Sample Hydrolyzed	Methionine, G./16 g. N	Methionine Sulfoxide G./16 g. N	% of total
Cockroach protein	2.00	0.23	10.3
Protein plus methionine	9.03	0.64	6.7
Methionine	7.24	0.13	1.8

Quantitative data (Table III) show that little oxidation occurs when a pure sample of methionine is treated with hot alkali and chromatographed. A greater amount occurs when methionine is subjected to the conditions of alkaline hydrolysis in the presence of protein. However, if the protein sulfoxide value is deducted from the total sulfoxide value of this sample, the percentage of methionine sulfoxide is found to be considerably lower than the 10% usually found in cockroach protein.

In a replicate experiment, cockroaches were extracted with 80% ethanol and a portion of the proteinaceous residue was treated with ethyl ether to determine the effect, if any, of ether which may contain peroxides. This and an untreated portion were then hydrolyzed in alkali and chromatographed. The actual quantities per unit of nitrogen were not determined but the ratios of methionine to methionine sulfoxide were in the same order as those indicated in Table III. The ethyl ether had no effect.

The remainder of the above sample was hydrolyzed with added methionine in alkali, and, as in Table III, a smaller percentage of methionine sulfoxide was found than when cockroach protein was hydrolyzed alone. The data are, therefore, in accord with the results obtained using the isotope method.

Adsorption Data. Considering the possibility that the methionine sulfoxide found in cockroach tissue hydrolyzates might be due to adsorption of soluble methionine sulfoxide to active sites on proteins, polypeptides, etc., the adsorption check described in a previous section was conducted. The data in Table IV show that, under the conditions used, more than 99% of exogenous methionine sulfoxide is removed even before the final steps in the extraction procedure. A maximum of

Table IV. Efficiency of Two Extraction Procedures in Removal of Soluble Methionine Sulfoxide-S^{35} from Tissues

Extraction Method	Fraction	C.P.M.	% of Total
Ethanol 80%	Hot 80% ethanol	9,830	90.58
	Cold 80% ethanol		
	1st wash	874	8.05
	2nd wash	100	0.92
	3rd wash	16	0.14
	Residue after acid hydrolysis	32	0.29
Total		10,852	99.98
Trichloroacetic acid 5%	Hot 5% trichloroacetic acid	8,518	95.78
	Cold 5% trichloroacetic acid	306	3.44
	Water	49	0.55
	Combined HCl-ethanol and ether fractions	9	0.10
	Residue after acid hydrolysis	11	0.12
Total		8,893	99.99

0.3% is adsorbed. Analysis of the data from the other experiments shows that the quantity of methionine sulfoxide in the protein fraction of the German cockroach is greatly in excess of this.

Other Combined Amino Acids. The data from two chromatographic analyses on chromobead resin and one on Amberlite IR-120 were averaged to give the data shown in Table V. The tryptophan value is from a

Table V. Amino Acids of German Cockroach Protein

Amino acid	Grams Amino Acids/16 Grams N		Hydrolyzing Medium
	Male	Female	
Arginine	7.3	7.0	Acid
Histidine	4.3	4.6	
Lysine	9.2	9.5	
Tyrosine	8.2	7.4	
Phenylalanine	5.0	5.4	
Cystine	1.0	0.6	
Methionine	2.1	2.8	
Serine	5.0	5.1	
Threonine	4.8	4.8	
Leucine	8.9	8.7	
Isoleucine	5.1	4.8	
Valine	8.1	7.9	
Glutamic acid	13.9	13.0	
Aspartic acid	10.1	10.1	
Glycine	9.0	8.1	
Alanine	10.5	8.9	
Proline	6.0	6.1	
β-Alanine	0.2	0.2	
Methionine sulfoxide	0.2		Alkali
Tryptophan	1.1		

single determination on the 15-cm. column of Amberlite IR-120. Except for the sulfur amino acids, there appear to be no sex-linked differences. Moreover, since cystine and methionine are both subject to considerable destruction with boiling hydrochloric acid, the values given for these amino acids should be substantiated by other methods.

The presence of β-alanine is unusual in that this amino acid is generally thought to be nonexistent in proteins. It is normally found either uncombined or as a constituent of small peptides such as anserine and carnosine.

Conclusions

The results of both paper and ion exchange chromatography indicate that methionine sulfoxide contributes to a small extent to the sulfur amino acid content of proteins and/or insoluble peptides of the German cockroach. Neumann, Moore, and Stein (12) report that traces of methionine sulfoxide are found in alkaline hydrolyzates of ribonuclease, lysozyme, trypsinogen, pepsin, catalase, chymotrypsinogen, bovine serum albumin, and some other proteins. The results of analysis of alkaline hydrolyzates of pepsin and bovine serum albumin by the authors indicate that methionine sulfoxide may amount to as much as 6.5% of the total weight of reduced and oxidized methionine. This amount may be expected as a result of oxidation during storage, hydrolysis, and chromatography (see Table III). Many of the proteins listed were obtained from commercial sources and were probably isolated without the precautions taken in the present experiments to prevent oxidation.

The function, if any, of methionine sulfoxide residues in peptides or proteins is a matter of conjecture. There is no evidence that they are of any structural significance. Indeed, since various enzymes such as ribonuclease and chymotrypsin are either partially or completely inactivated by oxidation of the methionine residues (15, 16), one hesitates to suggest any functional role for the sulfoxide. However, a role in the maintenance of oxidation-reduction potential of a biological system, as suggested by Dent (3), is conceivable.

Kennaugh (8) reports changes in the quantity of β-alanine in the cuticle of the American cockroach, Periplaneta americana (L.), during hardening and tanning, but it is not clear whether this represents free or combined β-alanine. Data presented herein and additional unpublished material indicate that the β-alanine is, indeed, a constituent of the cuticular protein.

The molar ratios of most of the amino acids in the protein of the German cockroach are generally similar to those of vertebrates and other invertebrates with respect to whole animal protein hydrolyzates (1). However, histidine, lysine, tyrosine, leucine, isoleucine, valine, and alanine are somewhat more abundant in cockroach protein and there is less cystine. The data vary significantly from data previously reported on the amino acid composition of the German cockroach (7). The earlier analysis, however, was conducted on insects with the entire head and digestive tract removed and the remaining portions of the body extracted with lipide solvents only.

Acknowledgment

The authors express their appreciation to Pierre Fromageot, Saclay, France, for his valuable suggestions and to W. J. Ray, Jr., Rockefeller Institute, New York, and D. E. Koshland, Jr., Brookhaven National Laboratory, Upton, N. Y., for their advice on alkaline hydrolysis.

Literature Cited

(1) Block, R. J., Weiss, K. W., "Amino Acid Handbook," p. 344, Charles C. Thomas, Springfield, Ill., 1956.

(2) Dent, C. E., Biochem. J. 43, 169 (1948).
(3) Dent, C. E., Science 105, 335 (1947).
(4) Fuller, R. C., Ibid., 124, 1253 (1956).
(5) Henry, S. M., Block, R. J., Contribs. Boyce Thompson Inst. 20, 317 (1960).
(6) Ibid., 21, 129 (1961).
(7) Hilchey, J. D., Block, R. J., Ibid., 17, 380 (1954).
(8) Kennaugh, J. H., J. Insect Physiol. 2, 97 (1958).
(9) Lo, T., Dixon, J. S., Li, C. H., Biochim. Biophys. Acta 53, 584 (1961).
(10) Margolis, D., Mandl, R. H., Contribs. Boyce Thompson Inst. 19, 509 (1958).
(11) Mizell, M., Simpson, S. B., Jr., J. Chromatog. 5, 157 (1961).
(12) Neumann, N. P., Moore, S., Stein, W. H., Biochemistry 1, 68 (1962).
(13) Nomoto, M., Narahashi, Y., Murakami, M., J. Biochem. (Tokyo) 48, 593 (1960).
(14) Piez, K. A., Morris, L., Anal. Biochem. 1, 187 (1961).
(15) Ray, W. J., Jr., Koshland, D. E., Jr., Brookhaven Symp. Biol. No. 13, 135 (1960).
(16) Ray, W. J., Jr., Koshland, D. E., Jr., J. Biol. Chem. 237, 2493 (1962).
(17) Spackman, D. H., Stein, W. H., Moore, S., Anal. Chem. 30, 1190 (1958).

Received November 30, 1962. Research aided by Grant E-2608, National Institutes of Health, U. S. Public Health Service, Bethesda, Md.,

8
Amino Acid Transport in Bacteria
Effect of Nutritional and Physiological Factors

JOSEPH T. HOLDEN

Department of Biochemistry,
Medical Research Institute,
City of Hope Medical Center,
Duarte, Calif.

The uptake and accumulation of various amino acids in <u>Lactobacillus arabinosus</u> have been described. Deficiencies of vitamin B_6, biotin, and pantothenic acid markedly alter the operation of these transport systems. Accumulation capacity is decreased most severely by a vitamin B_6 deficiency. This effect appears to arise indirectly from the synthesis of abnormal cell wall which renders the transport systems unusually sensitive to osmotic factors. Kinetic and osmotic experiments also exclude biotin and pantothenate from direct catalytic involvement in the transport process. Like vitamin B_6, they affect uptake indirectly, probably through the metabolism of a structural cell component. The evidence presented supports a concept of pool formation in which free amino acids accumulate in the cell through the intervention of membrane-localized transport catalysts.

Bacteria have been shown to accumulate amino acids against large apparent concentration gradients, utilizing systems which function maximally when coupled to energy-producing reactions; Holden (22) gives a detailed summary. It is still not possible to describe any part of this process in molecular terms. There is some evidence that pools of accumulated amino acids exist in an osmotically active and, presumably, unbound form (2, 8, 22), thereby implying that uptake occurs by a membrane-localized active transport process. A more detailed discussion of the reaction mechanism still requires speculation largely unsupported by evidence derived from studies on amino acid transport. Indeed, even these vague "hypotheses" rely heavily on findings obtained with inorganic ion and carbohydrate transport systems.

This paper summarizes an extensive effort to modify the activity of amino acid transport systems by rendering bacteria deficient in various B complex vitamins. It was hoped that this approach might provide some clues to the nature of the catalysts involved in transport either because the vitamin cofactor is involved directly in this process or indirectly because the vitamin might be concerned in the availability of such a catalyst. We were greatly influenced in this direction by the provocative findings of Christensen and coworkers (8, 10), who showed that the amount of amino acid accumulated by Ehrlich ascites tumor cells was greatly stimulated by pyridoxal. This led to the proposal that the vitamin serves as a carrier for amino acids during entry through the cell membrane. Although the studies described here revealed a number of instances in which vitamin deficiencies modify the course of amino acid accumulation, none of the effects seems to arise from the direct participation of the vitamin in the transport process.

General Characteristics of Amino Acid Transport in Lactobacillus
Transport in Lactobacillus arabinosus

The experiments discussed were performed with Lactobacillus arabinosus using glutamic acid, alanine, and proline as the test amino acids. The detailed experimental procedures have been described (21, 23, 27). Washed resting cells are incubated in a phosphate buffer with the radioactive amino acid, centrifuged, and extracted to release the amino acid, which is then measured enzymatically or by isotopic methods.

Figure 1 summarizes the accumulation of these amino acids within L. arabinosus during incubation in buffer containing glucose. There is little or no accumulation of the amino acid in the absence of a fermentable carbohydrate, indicating an energy requirement in the process. The amino acids can be released by brief exposure of the cells to boiling water, warm 75% ethanol, or cold 5% TCA (trichloroacetic acid). The close correspondence between enzymatically determined L-glutamic acid and the amount of this substance predicted from the isotope content of cell extracts shows that there is little metabolic loss of this amino acid. There is some (5 to 10%) conversion of L- to D-glutamic acid and small amounts of glutamine are formed. Radioautography revealed no significant conversion of proline or alanine to chromatographically distinguishable metabolites.

The large amounts of amino acid taken up enter these cells in opposition to sizable concentration gradients. At the external concentrations described above (Figure 1) and assuming an intracellular accessible water volume of 1.95 ml. per gram (cell mass refers to dry weight) (21), the ratios of internal to external concentrations are: glutamic acid, 111; alanine, 31; proline, 26. It is assumed that the amino acids are not bound and that they are uniformly distributed throughout the available cell water. The external concentrations normally used exceed those which saturate the internal capacity. At lower levels the concen-

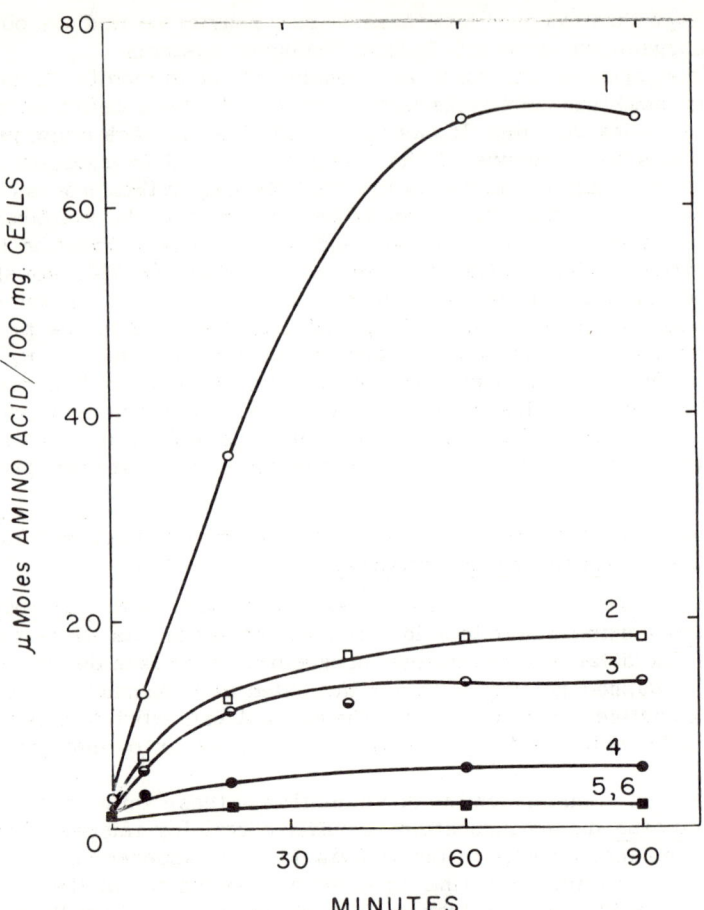

Figure 1. Accumulation of (1) glutamic acid, (2) alanine, and (3) proline in L. arabinosus

Incubation at 37° in presence of glucose. Curves 4, 5, and 6 show relatively low accumulation of amino acids in absence of glucose. Detailed experimental procedures (27)

tration ratios are considerably higher, reaching a value of 390 for glutamic acid.

The initial rate of uptake also increases as the external concentration is raised (Figure 2). At high concentrations further increments in the extracellular concentration produce much smaller increases in the accumulation rate, indicating the involvement of a saturable component in the uptake process. At low concentrations the data conform to the classical equation of Michaelis-Menten, giving a straight line when plotted according to the Lineweaver-Burk method. The rising slope of

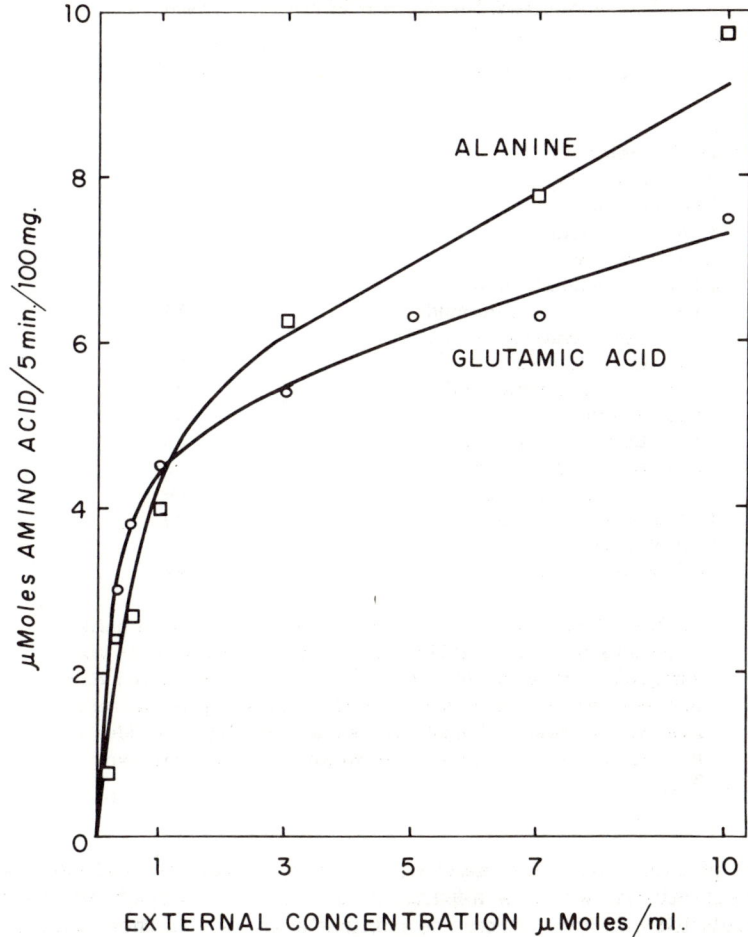

Figure 2. Effect of external concentration on initial accumulation rate of alanine and glutamic acid

All values derived from isotope content of cell extracts and corrected for uptake observed at 2° in absence of glucose

the curve at higher concentrations indicates the operation of a second component which is not saturated at levels up to 0.01 M.

The specificity of the process so far has been studied most extensively with the glutamate system using the technique of competition. As shown in Table I, a variety of substances diminish the rate of glutamate-C^{14} uptake when presented to the cells simultaneously with this amino acid. Glutamic-C^{12} acid served as a reference competitive substance. Glutamine is active and at very short incubation periods it sur-

Table I. Structural Specificity in Glutamate Accumulation

C^{12} Competitor	Relative Rate of Glutamate-C^{14} Entry [a]
None	100
L-Glutamic acid	38
D-Glutamic acid	85
L-Glutamine	59
L-Aspartic acid	50
L-Asparagine	89
DL-α-Aminoadipic acid	81
DL-β-Hydroxyglutamic acid	64
DL-α-Methylglutamic acid	59
α-Ketoglutaric acid	100
N-Acetyl-L-glutamic acid	90
Glutaric acid	100
DL-α-Aminobutyric acid	92
DL-α-Aminovaleric acid	89
DL-α,α'-Diaminoglutaric acid	100
L-Glutamic acid, γ-methyl ester	100
L-Ornithine	80
γ-Aminobutyric acid	92

[a] Uptake of L-C^{14}-glutamic acid after 5 min. at 37° from buffer containing this amino acid at 0.003M and no competitor was assigned a value of 100. Rates observed in the presence of competitor were recalculated on this basis to give the relative values shown. Competitive substrates were provided at 0.010M, except for racemic compounds, which were used at 0.020M.

passes glutamic acid in competing for entry. Aspartic acid also competes effectively, whereas asparagine has little or no affinity for the accumulation catalyst. From the relative activities of these analogs it is clear that both the α-amino and α-carboxyl groups are required for reaction with the accumulation catalyst. The γ-carboxyl group appears also to be required, although amide substitution as in glutamine is an acceptable modification, since it does not greatly reduce affinity for the hypothetical catalyst. The process shows a higher degree of stereospecificity than some other transport systems (4, 15, 33).

Because of the likely complexity of this process and the concomitantly minor probability of deriving mechanistically useful information from such studies, little attention has been given to the effects of pH on uptake beyond showing that glutamate accumulation is maximal between a pH of 6.0 and 6.5. This is close to the pH optimum for glycolysis in this organism. In agreement with the earlier findings of Gale (14), accumulated amino acids are retained tenaciously even during washing in distilled water. They can be eluted from the cells by those substances which are effective as competitors during uptake (Table I).

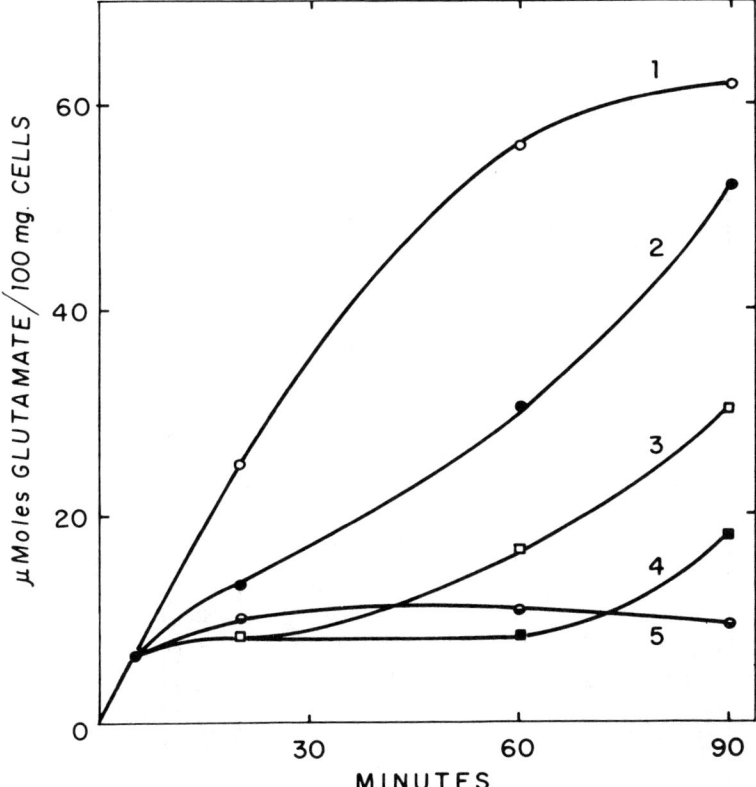

Figure 3. Effect of nutritional status and growth phase on time-course of glutamate accumulation

L. arabinosus cultured and harvested under following conditions:
1. Complete medium, cells harvested in mid-exponential phase at density of 0.35 mg./ml.
2. Complete medium, cells harvested in early exponential phase at density of 0.20 mg./ml.
3. Low biotin medium (0.050 mµg./ml.) cells harvested in period of declining growth rate at a density of 0.15 mg./ml.
4. Low pantothenic acid medium (7.5 mµg./ml.) cells harvested in period of declining growth rate at density of 0.23 mg./ml.
5. Low B_6 medium (0.020 mµg./ml.) cells harvested in period of declining growth rate at density of 0.19 mg./ml.
Washed cells incubated with C^{14}-glutamic acid under standard uptake conditions (27). Glutamate uptake estimated from isotope content of cell extracts

Effect of Vitamin Deficiencies on Amino Acid Uptake

The cellular content of various vitamins such as niacin, biotin, pantothenic acid, and vitamin B_6 can be reduced to low levels by cultivating L. arabinosus in media containing trace amounts of these substances. Having explored some of the properties of the transport systems in nutritionally normal cells, this study was extended to an investigation of these systems in various vitamin-deficient cell types. Figure 3 summarizes the course of glutamic acid accumulation in some of these nutritional variants. Since these deficiencies generally reduce the cell yield, nutritionally normal cells harvested at comparably low densities were used as controls. The accumulation rate of all low density cell types declines markedly after a brief period of normal accumulation. There is no further accumulation by severely vitamin B_6-deficient cells. In all other low density cell types the accumulation rate subsequently increases with longer incubation. The onset of this phase is postponed by a biotin deficiency, and by a pantothenic acid deficiency to an even greater extent.

Because vitamin B_6 has been considered prominently as a potential carrier for amino acids in cellular transport, the effects of this deficiency were investigated intensively. As shown in Figure 4, a vitamin B_6 deficiency also has a pronounced effect on proline and alanine accumulation. A large number of experiments with vitamin B_6-deficient cells (LB_6 cells, grown in absence or presence of trace amounts of pyridoxamine) showed that although there was a marked reduction in total glutamic acid accumulation, there was no effect on the initial uptake rate. Pretreatment of LB_6 cells with various B_6 inhibitors such as isonicotinic acid hydrazide, semicarbazide, or hydroxylamine did not depress the initial rate. The bacteria used in these experiments contained an average of only 40 molecules of vitamin B_6 per cell. The activities of various B_6-dependent enzymes such as the glutamic acid decarboxylase, and the aspartic-glutamic transaminase were depressed markedly in these cells. Consequently, the attainment of a normal accumulation rate is not easily reconciled with the suggestion that the vitamin functions as a carrier molecule. If this were true for this bacterium, there should have been fewer effective carrier molecules in the deficient cells and, therefore, a substantially reduced rate of uptake.

The lack of effect of a vitamin B_6 deficiency on the initial accumulation rate contrasts with the marked effect of this deficiency on the total amount of amino acid taken up. Treatment of deficient cells with various forms of vitamin B_6 alone failed to improve the accumulation capacity. Similarly, vitamin B_6 antagonists failed to reduce the capacity of nutritionally normal cells. Both observations suggested that the vitamin affects accumulation capacity indirectly and not by direct intervention of a vitamin B_6-dependent catalyst in the uptake process. Simultaneously, it was observed that LB_6 cells are morphologically abnormal, having a swollen, bulged appearance (26), and that they release large quantities of 260 mμ-absorbing materials including nucleotides during incubation in buffers (19). It became apparent that LB_6 cells might be deficient in cell wall substance, thus accounting for the morphological change. The decline in amino acid accumulation activity could be derived indirectly from this primary structural defect, possibly through a secondary change in the configuration of a membrane-localized transport catalyst.

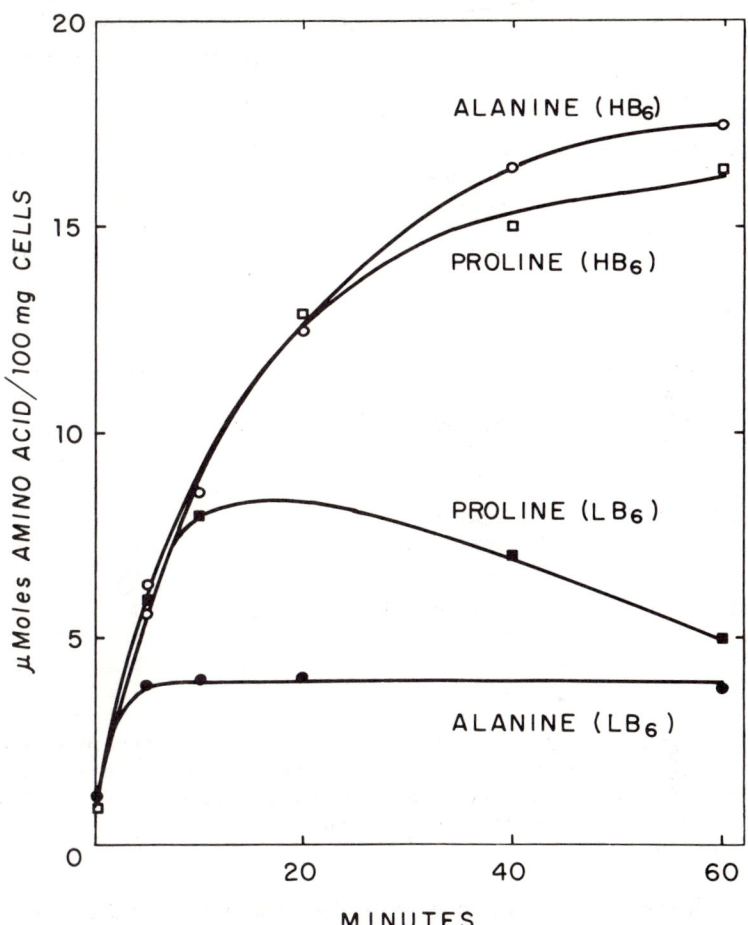

Figure 4. Effect of vitamin B_6-deficiency in L. arabinosus on alanine and proline accumulation

Washed cells incubated under standard uptake conditions with the C^{14}-amino acid at 0.003M. Accumulation estimated from isotope content of hot water cell extracts

In accord with this interpretation, it was observed that high concentrations of sucrose, KCl, and other ionic and nonionic substances restored the accumulation capacity of LB_6 cells to normal levels (Table II). The completely osmotic nature of this effect is supported by the findings summarized in Figure 5, which shows that except at very high levels sucrose and KCl have precisely equal stimulatory effects on glutamate accumulation over a wide range of iso-osmotic concentrations. In contrast to the tenacious retention of accumulated amino acids by nutritionally normal cells, LB_6 cells, which have accu-

Table II. Stimulation of Glutamate Accumulation by Various Substances[a]

Degree of Activity	Compound	% of Maximum Stimulation		
		0.3 M	0.6 M	0.9 M
High stimulation	Sucrose	47	92	100
	Glucose	32	66	72
	Galactose	16	45	57
	Lysine	50	74	74
	KCl	58	97	91
	KBr	46	85	76
	KNO_3	50	80	61
	NH_4Cl	70	85	71
Moderate stimulation	Sorbitol	10	34	48
	Fructose	7	13	24
	Potassium acetate	22	30	I[b]
	NaCl	40	51	I
	$MgCl_2$	71	22	I
No stimulation	Glycerol	0	0	0
	Rhamnose	0	0	0
	Ribose	9	0	0
Inhibition	Potassium lactate	15	I	I
	Glycine	I	I	I
	KH_2PO_4	I	I	I
	KCNS	I	I	I

[a] L. arabinosus (LB_6) was incubated for 90 min. under standard uptake conditions modified to include test substance at stated concentration. The results were taken from a number of experiments, in all of which sucrose was used as a reference stimulatory compound.
[b] I = inhibition.

mulated a large pool in the presence of sucrose, rapidly lose this additional portion of the pool when suspended in media of substantially lower osmolality. The abnormal accumulations of alanine and proline in LB_6 cells also are corrected by sucrose and KCL, showing that these defects have a common basis.

It seemed clear that sucrose has a beneficial effect on accumulation because it reduces water content in some portion of the cell. This region of the cell, therefore, should not be penetrated by sucrose. Consequently, thick suspensions of cells were exposed to various substances to determine what portion of the cell space accessible to a nonstimulatory substance (glycerol) is not entered by a stimulatory substance (sucrose).

As shown in Table III, sucrose enters nutritionally normal cells only to a slightly greater extent than dextran and inulin, which are confined to the extracellular compartment. The small differences between these values may arise from the more complete distribution of sucrose in cell wall interstices. In contrast, glycerol, a substance which is known to enter many cells rapidly and which does not stimu-

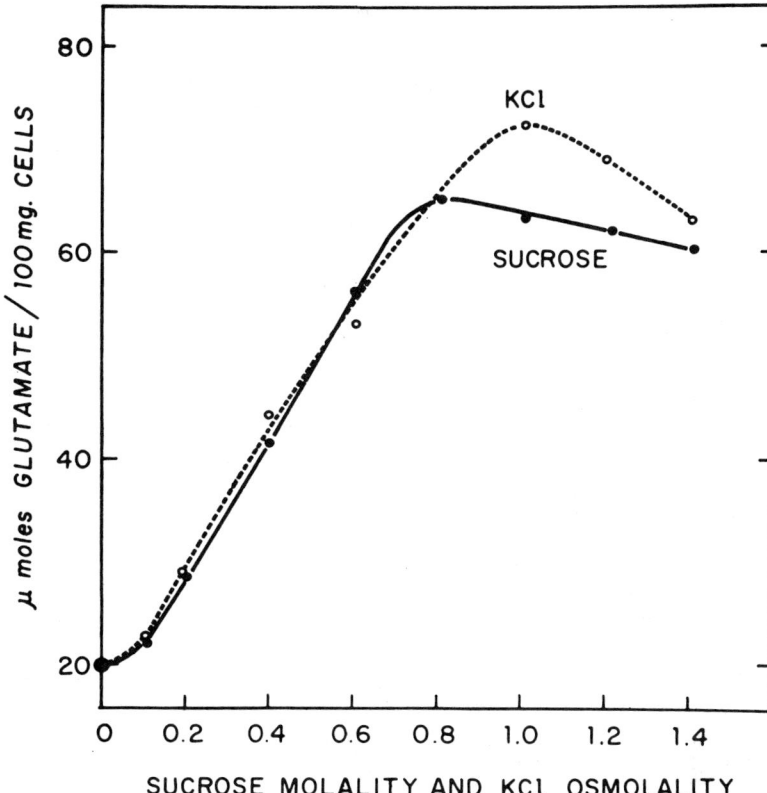

Figure 5. Comparative effectiveness of sucrose and KCl in stimulating glutamate accumulation by LB_6 cells

To maintain equal cell concentrations at equivalent levels of sucrose and CKl, amount of these substances required to give indicated molal concentration added to usual volume (3.45 ml.) of uptake buffer containing glucose and $L\text{-}C^{14}$-glutamic acid. Incubation for 100 minutes at 37°C. Amount of glutamate calculated from isotope content of cell extracts

late accumulation, penetrates all but approximately 28% of the pellet volume. Thus, in normal cells sucrose is excluded from the whole cell interior, probably by the peripheral cell membrane. In vitamin B_6-deficient cells these relationships are essentially the same. Sucrose appears to enter a slightly larger internal volume. However, these suspensions contain a higher proportion of nonviable cells which may be completely penetrated by sucrose. Therefore, it appears likely that here too sucrose is excluded from most or all the cell volume lying beneath the surface membrane and that it stimulates accumulation by preventing water influx to this region of the cell. While these results

Table III. Permeability of L. arabinosus to Sucrose and Glycerol[a]

Space Measured	Test Substance	Volume, Ml./G. DW	
		HB_6 cells	LB_6 cells
Total pellet		4.16	4.43
Total cell	Dextran	3.15	3.13
	Inulin	3.04	3.19
Sucrose impermeable	Sucrose	2.88	2.71
	C^{14}-Sucrose	2.50	2.33
Glycerol impermeable	C^{14}-Glycerol	1.15	1.28

[a] Approximately 100 mg. of centrifuged cells were resuspended and incubated at 37° for 15 or 45 min. in an equal volume of test substance dissolved in 0.12M phosphate buffer. Dextran (av. M.W. 60,000—90,000) was used at 100 mg./ml., inulin at 50 mg./ml., sucrose at 0.2 or 0.3M, and glycerol at 0.1M. Cells were centrifuged and supernatant analyzed as described (21). All incubations were in duplicate. Values shown are averages of 4 experiments with each cell type. Indicated spaces were obtained by subtracting volume accessible to test substance from total pellet volume.

are consistent with the accumulation model which assigns a prominent role to the cell membrane, they do not exclude the possibility that pools accumulate within intracellular sites which might be disrupted by overhydration of the cell interior.

Effect of Cell Wall Synthesis on Amino Acid Accumulation

As indicated above, the intimate relation between accumulation capacity and extracellular osmotic activity suggested that vitamin B_6-deficient cells might possess walls lacking normal rigidity. This inference has been substantiated in a number of ways. Most recently, the relative deficiency of wall substance in LB_6 cells has been demonstrated directly by electron microscopy (22) and by direct isolation (25). In a comparative study using various nutritional and physiological cell types, LB_6 cells yielded only 60% as much isolatable wall substance as did nutritionally normal cells harvested at a comparable density and growth phase. Most of this change represents a pronounced decrease in the amount of mucopeptide. The teichoic acid fraction was affected much less, suggesting that these major wall polymers may be synthesized independently of one another.

Earlier investigation of environmental factors which modify the accumulation capacity of LB_6 cells foreshadowed much of these findings. Specifically, it was observed that conditions which favor cell wall biosynthesis promote a large increase in amino acid accumulation capacity. These observations originated in the initial studies on osmotic protection when it was observed that LB_6 cells washed with vitamin B_6-

supplemented growth medium accumulated essentially normal amounts of glutamic acid, apparently because a small amount of growth medium was unavoidably carried with the cells into the uptake buffer (20). These small amounts of medium did not provide sufficient nutrients to support significant cell division, and, as shown in Table IV, the effect of growth

Table IV. Stimulation of Glutamate Accumulation by Growth Medium Components

Additions to Uptake Buffer	Glutamate Uptake, μmoles/100 Mg./90 Min.
None	20.0
Pyridoxamine	19.6
Growth medium	
$(+ B_6)$ [a]	50.4
$(- B_6)$	31.2
Growth medium components [b]	
Vitamin mix	20.3
Purines, pyrimidines $+ B_6$	23.2
Amino acids $+ B_6$	20.0
Buffer, trace salts $+ B_6$	54.0
Buffer-salts components [b]	
NH_4Cl, potassium acetate, B_6	54.7
$MnSO_4$, $MgCl_2$, KH_2PO_4, B_6	20.0

[a] 0.06 ml. used, volume calculated to be slightly in excess of that carried over when a cell pellet was washed with growth medium [cf. (28) for growth medium composition].
[b] At levels equal to those contained in 0.06 ml. of medium.

medium could be reproduced entirely by its buffer and trace element fraction. The effect of these components in turn was accounted for entirely by acetate, NH_4^+, and pyridoxamine. Under these conditions nearly normal accumulation capacity was achieved in the absence of osmotic protectants. These beneficial changes were observed in the absence of significant increases in intracellular protein and nucleic acid.

The effect of acetate is highly specific. Of a large variety of mono- and dicarboxylic acids tested, only a few such as pyruvate, butyrate, malate, and succinate stimulated uptake slightly even when tested at concentrations 5 times higher than those at which acetate is effective. Pyridoxamine was maximally effective at very low levels $(1 \times 10^{-9} M)$, indicating a catalytic role in this phenomenon. In the range where its concentration is limiting, the total amount of NH_4^+ available was lower than the additional glutamate accumulated.

A clearer indication of the stimulatory mechanism came from pretreatment studies. These were attempted on the premise that if these substances are used to repair a cell wall defect, it should be possible to treat cells with acetate, NH_4^+, and vitamin B_6 and thereby bring them to a state in which they would accumulate amino acid normally in the absence of these stimulatory compounds or osmotic protectants. In such experiments LB_6 cells were pretreated in sucrose buffer with acetate, NH_4^+, and pyridoxamine, centrifuged away from these substances, and then exposed to glutamic-C^{14} acid under standard uptake conditions to measure their accumulation capacity. Initially, this procedure failed to produce any improvement in amino acid accumulation. However, as shown in Table V, the addition of glutamate-C^{12} to the pretreatment so-

Table V. Effect of Preincubation on Restoration of Glutamate Accumulation Activity in LB_6 Cells[a]

Preincubation Supplement	Time, min.	Uptake Condition	Glutamate (C^{14}) Accumulation, μmoles/100 Mg./90 Min.
Sucrose	0	Std [a]	9.9
	0	+ Mix [a]	52.6
	90	Std	13.6
+ mix [a]	90	Std	13.4
+ mix + L-glutamate (1 M)	90	Std	46.3

[a] LB_6 cells of L. arabinosus were preincubated under standard uptake conditions (27) with indicated supplements. Sucrose was used at 0.6M. Mix provides potassium acetate at a final concentration of 0.0023M, NH_4Cl at 0.0012M, and pyridoxamine at 0.18×10^{-6} M. After times shown cells were separated from this solution by centrifugation at $5000 \times g$ for 7 min., resuspended in cold buffer, and distributed to tubes for measurement of C^{14}-glutamate accumulation in normal way. Std. refers to standard uptake condition.

lution caused a large increase in the subsequently measured accumulation activity.

While this suggests that glutamate is an essential component of the pretreatment solution, an alternate possibility is that the cell must accumulate glutamate to protect or maintain an essential intracellular site. A number of observations conflict with the latter possibility. The amount of glutamate taken up and retained through the cycle of pretreatment and wash is only one half the additional amount of glutamate-C^{14} subsequently taken up. A more conclusive finding is that the capacity for alanine accumulation is not increased when alanine is provided during pretreatment, whereas there is a significant improvement when glutamic acid is included in the pretreatment solution.

While these results are consistent with the proposed involvement of the cell wall in the determination of accumulation capacity, they do not completely exclude changes in some other cell component which might be the primary locus of the described effects. Consequently, the fate of acetate-C^{14} in this organism was investigated. Table VI shows that the major sites of acetate incorporation in resting cells are the

Table VI. Distribution of Acetate-2-C^{14} in L. arabinosus Cell Fractions

Fraction	Cell Type	
	HB_6	LB_6
	CPM/10-Mg. Cells [a]	
Cold TCA	3,000	6,000
Hot TCA	100	300
Ethanol	114,000	128,000
Trypsin	1,600	500
Residue (wall)	38,000	19,000

[a] Washed cells were incubated at 1.6 mg./ml. in 0.12M phosphate buffer (27) containing glucose (0.028M), sucrose (0.5M), and potassium acetate-2-C^{14} (0.0059M). After 60 min. at 37° cells were centrifuged, pellets frozen and extracted as described by Park and Hancock (39). Appropriate aliquots were plated and radioactivity was measured in a gas-flow counter.

ethanol-soluble and the cell wall (specifically, mucopeptide) fractions. Vitamin B_6-deficient cells incorporate half as much acetate into the wall fraction as do nutritionally normal cells, but are as active as these control cells when NH_4^+, pyridoxamine, and L-glutamic acid are provided (22, 24). There is a sizable increase in cell wall substance under these conditions. Thus, those pretreatment conditions which foster a large increase in amino acid transport and accumulation activity in LB_6 cells are also required to obtain a level of acetate incorporation into cell wall comparable to that observed in HB_6 cells (grown with an excess of pyridoxamine).

Since we have been unable to detect changes in other cell fractions which correlate with improvements in accumulation capacity, it appears reasonable to conclude, especially in view of the previously cited osmotic evidence, that a lack in cell wall rigidity limits the accumulation capacity of LB_6 cells and that the repair of the wall defect suffices to permit these cells to express normal accumulation capacity. On the question of the participation of vitamin B_6 in amino acid transport, these, and especially the osmotic experiments, are clearly inconsistent with the suggested catalytic role of this substance directly in the entry reaction.

Stimulation of Accumulation in Other Vitamin-Deficient Cell Types

The unusual course of amino acid accumulation in biotin- and pantothenate-deficient cells (Figure 3) also has been found to be markedly influenced by sucrose and other osmotic protectants, as well as by acetate. The course of glutamic acid uptake by biotin-deficient cells in the

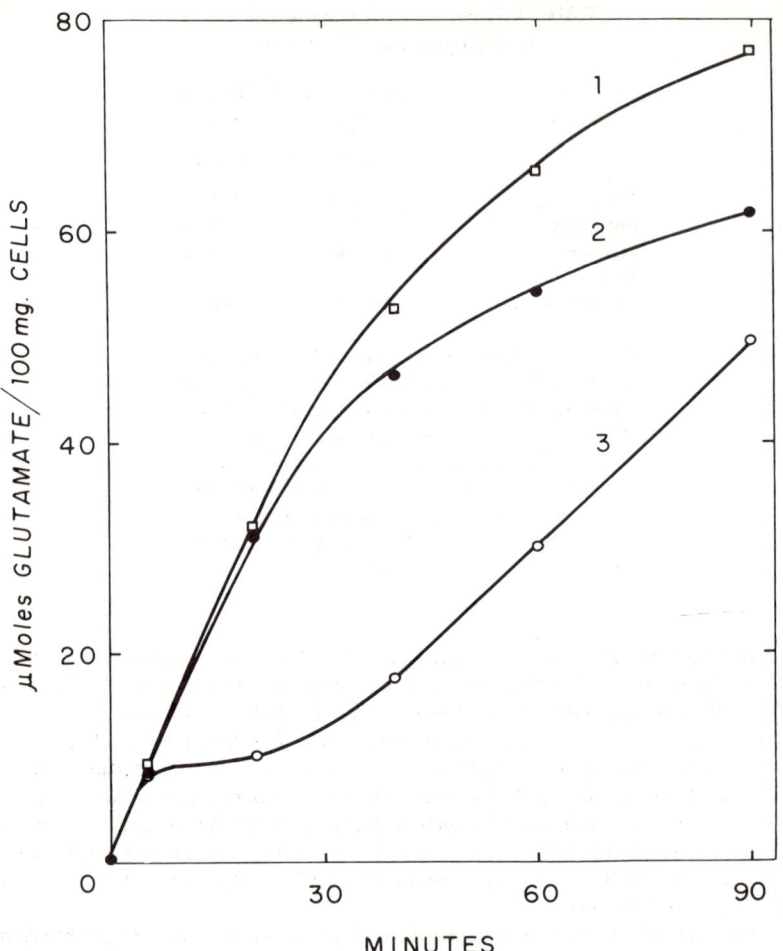

Figure 6. Effect of sucrose on abnormal glutamate accumulation observed in biotin-deficient cells of L. arabinosus

1. *Nutritionally normal control cells, glutamate uptake measured under standard conditions*
2. *Biotin-deficient cells, uptake measured in presence of 0.5M sucrose*
3. *Biotin-deficient cells, uptake measured under standard conditions*

Glutamate accumulation estimated from isotope content of hot water cell extracts

absence and presence of sucrose is described in Figure 6. The unusual biphasic time-course characterized by a marked decline in accumulation rate after 5 minutes of normal uptake is restored to the control pattern by high sucrose concentrations. Thus, as in a vitamin B_6 deficiency, a biotin deficiency has no effect on the rate or amount of amino acid taken up, so long as the cells are exposed to a high extracellular osmotic pressure. This suggests, first, that these cells also may possess structural features which are incompatible with the massive accumulation of amino acids, and, second, that this vitamin also does not play a catalytic role directly in the transport process. The same is true for pantothenate-deficient cells, which suffer even a more pronounced aberration in the uptake pattern (Figure 3) but which accumulate amino acids in a normal manner when extracellular sucrose is provided.

With biotin-deficient cells low concentrations of acetate will substitute for high concentrations of sucrose in restoring uptake to normal levels (22). Biotin stimulates slightly when provided in addition to acetate. Pantothenate-deficient cells respond dramatically to acetate only in the presence of this vitamin. This behavior probably reflects the involvement of coenzyme A in the process which restores a normal accumulation pattern.

Therefore, the three vitamin deficiencies so far studied in detail appear to affect amino acid transport and accumulation in similar but indirect ways. The accumulation defect is most pronounced in vitamin B_6-deficient cells, for which there is also strong evidence implicating an abnormality in cell wall composition as a likely source of the change in transport activity. Direct evidence for a cell wall change in biotin- and pantothenate-deficient cells has not yet been obtained. The possibility remains, therefore, that the change in accumulation activity may be caused by an abnormality in some other structural component such as the peripheral cell membrane.

Mechanism of Amino Acid Transport and Accumulation

These studies strongly contradict the suggestion that vitamin B_6 serves as a carrier of amino acids during transport, at least so far as L. arabinosus and related bacteria are concerned. They also cast serious doubt on the possibility that biotin and pantothenic acid are involved directly in this process. Recent studies with Ehrlich ascites tumor cells suggest that here too vitamin B_6 does not catalyze the entry step of transport (9, 38). On the other hand, Mora and Snell (37) have observed that pyridoxal does stimulate amino acid accumulation in protoplasts but not in whole cells of S. faecalis. As with Ehrlich ascites tumor cells relatively high levels of the vitamin are required to elicit the response. This finding, together with the observation that cells with external walls do not show the effect, suggests that a structural rather than a catalytic process may be affected. A number of studies have shown that vitamin B_6 may affect amino acid transport in intestinal tissue (31). However, the metabolic basis of this effect has not yet been evaluated.

The experiments reported here also have been useful in evaluating various current proposals regarding the nature of the accumulation process. The view is widely held that accumulations of the type described here can be attributed to the operation of transport catalysts localized in a permeability barrier which allows net inward fluxes to be maintained until high intracellular concentrations of free amino acids are attained. This thesis is supported by the repeated demonstration of a peripheral permeability barrier in bacteria (22, 35, 43). Although direct efforts to demonstrate sequestration of large amino acid pools in or on intracellular polymers or particulates have failed, and the extraction properties of these pools are consistent with their occurrence in a free form, incontrovertible evidence supporting this view is still lacking. Indeed, after careful analysis some workers interpret their findings on amino acid uptake in E. coli in terms of fixation on adsorption sites following entrance catalyzed by mobile carriers (6, 7). The most convenient experimental measure of the state of the pool seems to be its in situ osmotic activity. There have been a number of attempts to determine such activity (1, 22, 36). While amino acids within bacterial protoplasts appear to cause water influx, measured indirectly as changes in light scattering, the studies reported so far have not been quantitatively precise enough to establish how much of the pool participates in this phenomenon. Although they are a good deal less direct, the studies reported here are of interest from this point of view.

An obvious interpretation of our findings is that the newly accumulated amino acid pool is free and that an increased intracellular osmotic pressure may be developed in the course of its uptake. Under most circumstances the cell wall is sufficiently rigid to prevent any adverse effects arising from the resultant stress. However, in vitamin B_6-deficient cells, and possibly in other deficient types as well, wall rigidity is decreased and the increasing osmotic pressure associated with accumulation causes membrane distention or some other configurational modification which is deleterious to the uptake process. Consequently, a greatly diminished pool size is attained unless the increased intracellular osmotic pressure is offset by a greatly elevated extracellular osmotic pressure. Unfortunately, this simple interpretation of our osmotic findings is not strongly supported when the quantitative aspects of this phenomenon are considered.

Figure 7 shows that as the sucrose concentration is raised increments in alanine and proline accumulation fall along a straight line having the same slope. Alanine capacity, being higher, required higher concentrations of sucrose for maximum accumulation. However, approximately 4 μmoles per ml. of extracellular sucrose were required to stimulate an additional intracellular alanine or proline load of only 1 μmole per ml. (assuming uniform distribution of these amino acids in the available cell water). If these substances have activity coefficients in the vicinity of unity, it would appear either that other substances contribute to the osmotic load or that the amino acids are sequestered in a fraction of the cell water with a corresponding increase of concentration in this region. The behavior of glutamic acid is more easily reconciled with the simple concept of direct osmotic interplay of extracellular sucrose and intracellular amino acid. In the range 0.2 to 0.5M sucrose, an increase of 2 μmoles per ml. in extracellular sucrose concentration permits an apparent increase of 0.84 μmole per ml. of intracellular glutamate. These values at least approach the ratio ex-

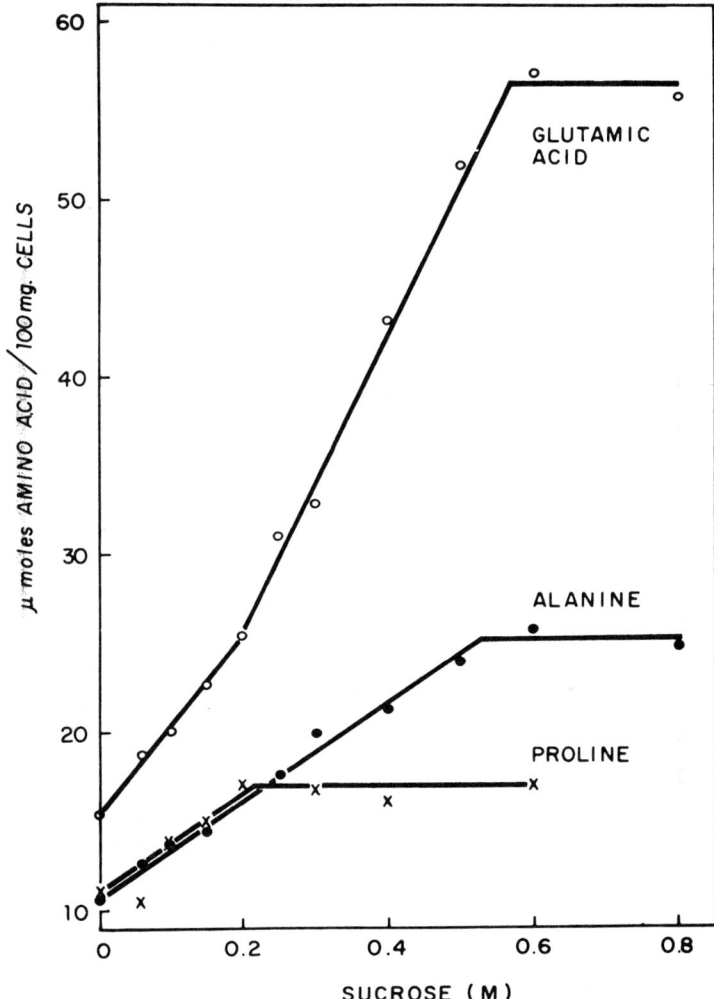

Figure 7. Comparative stimulation of glutamic acid, alanine, and proline accumulation in vitamin B_6-deficient cells of L. arabinosus at various extracellular sucrose concentrations

Incubation at 37° for 60 minutes using indicated sucrose concentration in standard uptake buffer containing L-C^{14}-amino acid at 0.003M. Accumulation calculated from isotope content of hot water cell extracts

pected if there was osmotic interaction (somewhat less than two assuming that at the intracellular pH glutamate behaves as a uni-univalent ion of the monobasic salt). Thus, in quantitative terms this portion of the investigation gives only rather limited support to the concept of free intracellular amino acid pools.

Further support comes from the studies relating cell wall biosynthesis and amino acid accumulation capacity in vitamin B_6-deficient cells, since it is difficult to account for these observations without attributing considerable osmotic activity to the accumulated amino acids. Any description of accumulation which invokes amino acid attachment to intracellular binding sites, whose affinity can be reduced by a vitamin B_6 deficiency, must account for the stimulation of uptake that accompanies the synthesis of essentially extracellular cell wall material. If the reduction in affinity occurs because the cell interior becomes overhydrated (a reasonable postulate which follows from the osmotic experiments), the beneficial effect of wall synthesis is not readily explicable, since vitamin B_6-deficient cells have a swollen appearance which is not significantly altered after wall synthesis has been stimulated. Thus, the existing overhydration within the cell probably is not reversed by this change. In contrast, the deposition of additional wall substance would prevent further unfavorable consequences of swelling such as membrane distention, and, in this way, forestall the premature cessation of amino acid accumulation.

Although these results appear to be most reasonably accounted for in terms of an osmotically active pool which is largely unassociated with intracellular binding sites, the speculative nature of these proposals is clearly appreciated, as is the necessity for more definitive information. For example, while our evidence clearly shows an association between improvements in uptake activity and synthesis of wall substance, it does not exclude the concomitant synthesis of small amounts of functionally important membrane substance. Furthermore, alternative proposals are conceivable that would account for all our findings without necessarily invoking the occurrence of an osmotically active pool. One is that vitamin B_6 might act as an essential component of a regulatory mechanism which controls the movement of water through the cell membrane. The difficulty of excluding such a proposal underscores the limitations of existing evidence concerning the mechanism of pool formation and retention.

Recent studies of inorganic ion transport have revealed possible relations to ATP metabolism (40, 42), phospholipide turnover (18), phosphoprotein turnover (3, 32), and oxidative phosphorylation (5, 41). These studies have opened fresh approaches to this problem and have raised hopes that some insight into the mechanism of ion transport will soon be attained. In contrast, progress in studies on amino acid transport has been somewhat less dramatic.

A number of workers have observed amino acids in lipid extracts, including those of microbial origin (11, 12, 17, 29). Recently, Macfarlane (34) has reported that most of the phospholipide in Clostridium welchii is bound to amino acids and that some of this material occurs as the O-amino acid ester of phosphatidylglycerol. The relatively prominent occurrence of lipides in cell membranes has led to the recurrent suggestion that transport of hydrophilic substances through such membranes would be greatly facilitated by combination with hydrophobic substances. Consequently, most workers who have observed the incorporation of amino acids into lipid fractions quite naturally have mentioned the possibility that these lipoamino acid complexes are related to the transport process (13, 16, 29, 30, 34). As yet, there have been no definitive observations favoring this view, and some instances of contrary findings. For example, Hunter and Goodsall (29) have observed that chloramphenicol inhibits lipoamino acid synthesis in B. megaterium without affecting the uptake of amino acids into the pool. This finding tends to support an alternative proposal which has perhaps been quoted even more widely, that lipoamino acid complexes are concerned in protein synthesis.

It is apparent that at this stage of development definitive conclusions are premature, and that this aspect of amino acid and lipide metabolism will be pursued vigorously in the near future. It is of considerable interest to us that biotin and pantothenic acid deficiencies affect amino acid transport in L. arabinosus, since both vitamins are known to play a prominent role in lipide biosynthesis. We are currently re-examining the turnover of lipide fractions in nutritionally normal and vitamin-deficient cell types to determine whether there is some relation between this aspect of metabolism and amino acid transport. In any case, the nature of the catalytic steps involved in amino acid transport is still unknown to us. They probably occur in the peripheral cell membrane, but even this elementary and widely accepted belief will require additional study before it can be accepted beyond doubt as an established fact.

Summary

The uptake and accumulation of various amino acids in Lactobacillus arabinosus have been described. An extensive investigation of this process using cells deficient in vitamin B_6, biotin, and pantothenic acid has shown that all these deficiencies markedly alter the transport process. Accumulation capacity is most severely decreased by a vitamin B_6 deficiency. The evidence now available indicates that this does not reflect the direct participation of the vitamin in the transport process, but rather is an indirect effect arising from the synthesis of an abnormal cell wall which renders the cell unusually sensitive to osmotic stress. Amino acid transport in vitamin B_6-deficient cells is restored to normal levels by raising the extracellular osmotic pressure or by enabling the cells to synthesize additional wall substance.

These findings can be interpreted to support a concept of pool formation in which free amino acids accumulate within the cell through the intervention of membrane-localized transport catalysts. The nature of these catalysts is still unknown. The kinetic and osmotic experiments reported here also appear to exclude biotin and pantothenic acid from direct involvement in the transport process. The evidence suggests that like vitamin B_6 they affect transport indirectly through some change in the synthesis or turnover of a structural component of the cell.

Acknowledgment

The author is indebted to the following associates for assistance in carrying out these studies: Jane Holman, Marilyn Maile, Josephus Van Balgooy, and Nedra Utech.

Literature Cited

(1) Abrams, A., in "Amino Acid Pools," by J. T. Holden, p. 764, Elsevier, Amsterdam, 1962.
(2) Abrams, A., Yamasaki, G., Redman, J., Mackenzie, C. G., Federation Proc. 19, 129 (1960).
(3) Ahmed, K., Judah, J. D., Wallgren, H., Biochim. Biophys. Acta 69, 428 (1963).
(4) Boezzi, J. A., De Moss., R. D., Ibid., 49, 471 (1961).
(5) Brierley, G. P., Murer, E., Green, D. E., Science 140, 60 (1963).
(6) Britten, R. J., McClure, F. T., Bact. Rev. 126, 292 (1962).
(7) Britten, R. J., McClure, F. T., in "Amino Acid Pools," by J. T. Holden, p. 595, Elsevier, Amsterdam, 1962.
(8) Christensen, H. N., in "Amino Acid Metabolism," by W. D. McElroy and B. Glass, p. 63, Johns Hopkins Press, Baltimore, 1955.
(9) Christensen, H. N., in "Amino Acid Pools," by J. T. Holden, p. 612, Elsevier, Amsterdam, 1962.
(10) Christensen, H. N., Riggs, T. R., Coyne, B. A., J. Biol. Chem. 209, 413 (1954).
(11) Gaby, W. L., Naughton, R. N., Logan, C., Arch. Biochem. Biophys. 82, 34 (1959).
(12) Gaby, W. L., Silberman, R., Ibid., 87, 188 (1960).
(13) Gaby, W. L., Wolin, H. L., Zajac, I., Cancer Res. 20, 1508 (1960).
(14) Gale, E. F., Advan. Protein. Chem. 8, 287 (1953).
(15) Halvorson, H. O., Cohen, G. N., Ann. Inst. Pasteur 95, 73 (1958).
(16) Hendler, R. W., in "Amino Acid Pools," by J. T. Holden, p. 750, Elsevier, Amsterdam, 1962.
(17) Hendler, R. W., J. Biol. Chem. 234, 1466 (1959).
(18) Hokin, L. E., Hokin, M. R., Federation Proc. 22, 8 (1963).
(19) Holden, J. T., Biochim. Biophys. Acta 29, 667 (1958).
(20) Ibid., 33, 581 (1959).
(21) Ibid., 74, 401 (1963).
(22) Holden, J. T., "Amino Acid Pools," p. 566, Elsevier, Amsterdam, 1962.
(23) Holden, J. T., J. Biol. Chem. 234, 872 (1959).
(24) Holden, J. T., Proc. Fifth Intern. Congr. Biochem., p. 304, Moscow, 1961.
(25) Holden, J. T., unpublished manuscript.
(26) Holden, J. T., Holman, J., J. Bacteriol. 73, 592 (1957).
(27) Holden, J. T., Holman, J., J. Biol. Chem. 234, 865 (1959).
(28) Holden, J. T., Wildman, R. B., Snell, E. E., Ibid., 191, 559 (1951).
(29) Hunter, G. D., Goodsall, R. A., Biochem. J. 78, 564 (1961).
(30) Hunter, G. D., James, A. T., Nature 198, 789 (1963).
(31) Jacobs, F. A., Poston, J. M., Biochim. Biophys. Acta 51, 602 (1961).
(32) Judah, J. D., Ahmed, K., McLean, A. E. M., Ibid., 65, 472 (1962).
(33) Lark, K. G., Can. J. Microbiol. 5, 381 (1959).
(34) Macfarlane, M. G., Nature 196, 136 (1962).
(35) Mitchell, P., Ann. Rev. Microbiol. 13, 407 (1959).
(36) Mitchell, P., Moyle, J., in "Bacterial Anatomy," by E. T. C. Spooner and B. A. D. Stocker, p. 150, Cambridge Univ. Press, 1956.

(37) Mora, J., Snell, E. E., Biochemistry 2, 136 (1963).
(38) Oxender, D. L., Royer, M., Federation Proc. 20, 140 (1961).
(39) Park, J. T., Hancock, R., J. Gen. Microbiol. 22, 249 (1960).
(40) Post, R. L., Merritt, C. W., Kinsolving, C. R., Albright, C. D., J. Biol. Chem. 235, 1796 (1960).
(41) Rossi, C. S., Lehninger, A. L., Biochem. Biophys. Res. Commun. 11, 411 (1963).
(42) Skou, J. C., Biochim. Biophys. Acta 42, 6 (1960).
(43) Weibull, C., Ann. Rev. Microbiol. 12, 1 (1958).

Received July 26, 1963. Work supported by a grant from the U. S. Public Health Service (E-1487) and a contract between the Office of Naval Research and the City of Hope Medical Center [NONR-2702(00)].

9
Differential Responses to Amino Acids in Bacterial Growth

GERRIT TOENNIES

*The Institute for Cancer Research,
Philadelphia 11, Pa.*

> The paper discusses the changes which result during the growth of Streptococcus faecalis, when different essential amino acids are depleted while all other nutrients remain available in excess. Depletion of lysine, an amino acid which is a building block of cell wall glycopeptides as well as of protein, is followed by bacterial lysis, while depletion of other protein components is followed by further growth. The depletion of different amino acids elicits different changes in cellular composition, characterized by different proportions of protein, cell wall, membrane, DNA, RNA, etc. A tentative cytological interpretation of some of these changes is presented.

Richard Block's "Amino Acid Handbook" is a compendium of analytical procedures and analytical results. Among the analytical procedures a chapter is devoted to the microbiological methods, and it is from a study of microbiological methods for the determination of amino acids that the studies here summarized have developed. More detailed accounts of various phases of the work have been published (1-15).

Principle of Microbiological Assay

The principle of microbiological assay is simple. For instance, in order to determine, say, phenylalanine, one selects a microorganism that needs phenylalanine. In a medium which contains an abundance of all other nutrients, the extent of bacterial growth will be determined by the amount of phenylalanine added to the medium. The analyst will set up a series of tubes, standards and unknowns, and after inoculation put them in the incubator. After a specified period—overnight or several days—he will take the tubes out and either titrate the acidity formed as a result of the growth, or measure in the spectrophotometer the amount of turbidity formed. He is not likely to look at the tubes before the method calls for it, especially if he is a chemist who knows little about bacteria.

We happened to belong to this category, but just the same we did look at our tubes before they were ready for analysis—the reason being that we were unhappy about the lack of linearity of the responses. The response curves varied, not so much from one experiment to another, but strangely from one amino acid to another. This is how we came to study the growth curves.

On the left side of Figure 1 we see the turbidity curve with time

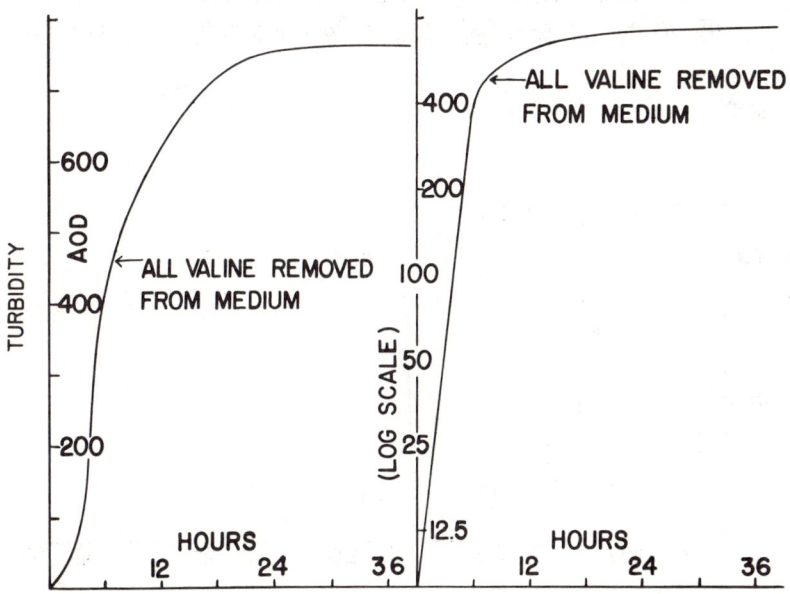

Figure 1. Growth in presence of 5.3×10^{-5} M L-valine

of a culture of S. faecalis which contains a limited concentration of valine. After 24 hours the curve has nicely leveled off, and this would seem to be the logical time to take the analytical readings. Eventually we came to determine the fate of a limiting amino acid over the whole course of bacterial growth. For instance, at various points along the growth curve we determined how much valine was present within the organism and how much was left in the medium. The sum of these two quantities remained constant, and equal to the amount added in the beginning—i.e., there was no metabolic loss. It was a little more surprising to find that the point at which all the valine had disappeared from the medium and was incorporated into the bacterial crop was not up at the plateau, but somewhere almost halfway down before the plateau was reached.

The right half of Figure 1 shows the same data as the left side, but the turbidity values are plotted on a l garithmic scale instead of the ordinary arithmetical scale. Under these conditions the first part of the growth curve is essentially as it should be if the bacteria grow at a constant rate of duplication or, as it is called, are in the exponential or log phase. Now the point at which all valine has been removed from the medium, which we call the depletion point, is close to the end of the exponential growth phase. In this case, as in the other cases discussed, after depletion of the limiting amino acid all other amino acids remain available in large excess.

Figure 2 shows additional examples. The depletion point is reached

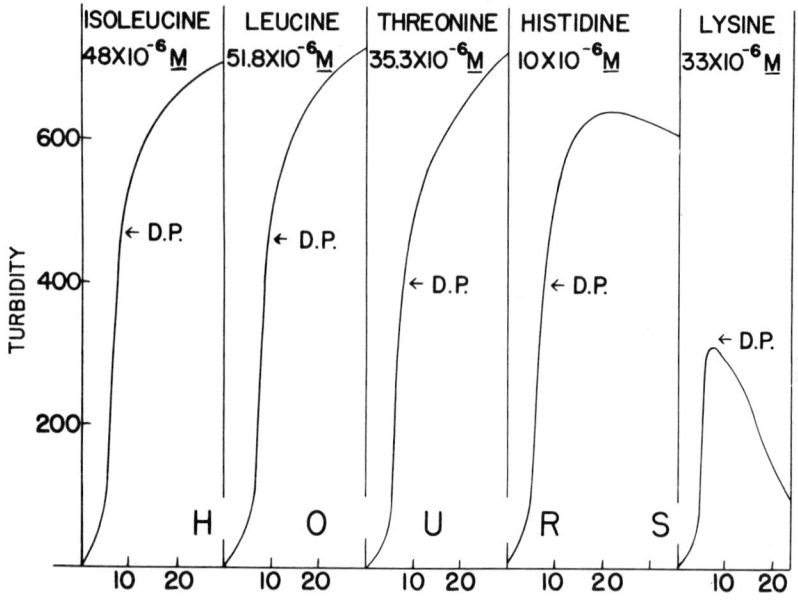

Figure 2. Growth patterns in response to different limiting amino acids

D. P. Depletion point

well before growth attains its maximum, and in every case tends to coincide with the end of the exponential phase.

Lysine is an interesting exception: The theoretical depletion point is not followed by further growth, but by prompt lysis and eventual disappearance of the culture.

Bacterial Cell Walls

This was the evidence some years ago. At that time studies began to appear in the literature about the composition of bacterial cell walls. It became evident that among the amino acids we had studied only lysine had been found as a major component of wall substance. Therefore, one could tentatively say that lysine is essential for the growth of the cell wall, but that isoleucine, leucine, threonine, histidine, valine, and some others are not. All of them are, of course, essential for cytoplasmic protein synthesis.

One could further conclude that at the depletion point (and the end of exponential growth) protein synthesis stops but wall synthesis continues. In the case of lysine depletion, however, both protein synthesis and wall synthesis are impossible, and in the absence of continuous renewal through new growth the cells fall victim to autolysis.

The shapes of the growth curves after the depletion point show characteristic and reproducible differences from one limiting amino acid to another. The most striking example of these differences is illustrated by Figure 3, in which the depletion points of a valine-limited

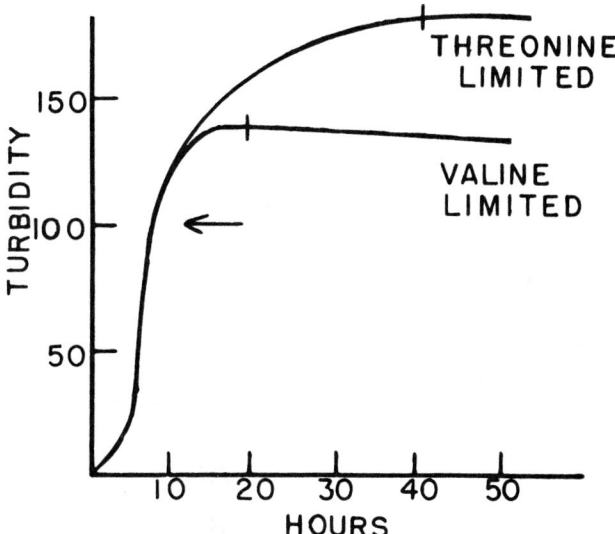

Figure 3. Comparison of valine- and threonine-limited growths

and a threonine-limited culture are both shown as 100 turbidity units. In the case of valine limitation postexponential growth amounts to about 40% and attains its maximum after 20 hours; in the case of threonine limitation the postexponential growth is twice as large and requires about twice as long.

To evaluate the possibility of postexponential cell wall synthesis occurring without protein synthesis, we disrupted bacteria by shaking with glass beads. Under proper conditions this yields a water-soluble and a water-insoluble fraction. As a first approximation the soluble fraction may be called the cytoplasmic fraction and the insoluble part the wall fraction. Figure 4 shows a study by the glass bead procedure of cells from the exponential growth phase and of 20-hour cells result-

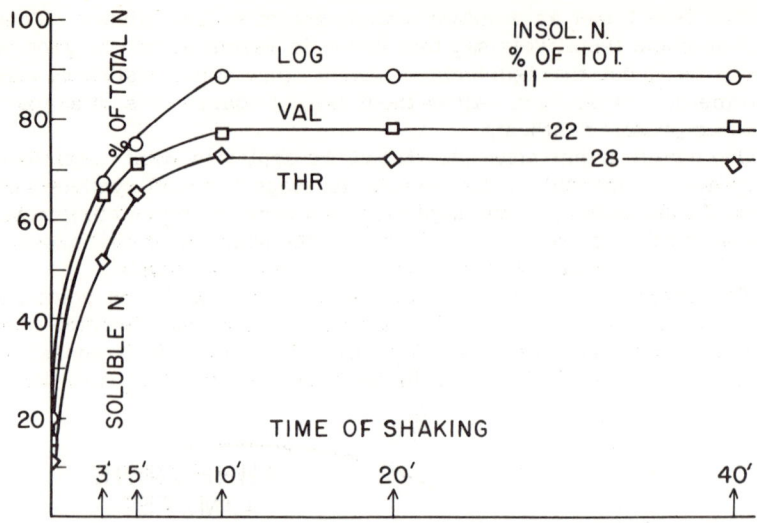

Figure 4. Mechanical disruption of exponential cells and valine- and threonine-limited postexponential cells

ing from valine depletion, as well as 40-hour cells resulting from threonine depletion. The graph shows the partition of the total nitrogen between the soluble and the insoluble fractions after different periods of mechanical disruption. The insoluble nitrogen fraction is 11% of the total for exponential cells, 22% for so-called valine cells, and 28% for threonine cells. This agrees well with our expectation that the valine cells are richer in wall substance than the log cells, and shows that the insoluble nitrogen fraction is largest in the threonine cells, where postexponential growth is twice as much as in valine cells.

The insoluble substance in all three cases turned out to be identical or very similar in composition and to represent nearly pure wall substance.

Nothing in these results gives any indication as to why the postexponential growth is twice as large in the case of threonine depletion as in valine depletion. It became obvious that in our anatomical analysis of different bacterial crops we had to go beyond the two compartments: soluble and insoluble fractions.

Bacterial Membrane

Particularly it became necessary to consider the bacterial membrane. As things stand now, the bacterial cell wall is thought of as an outer skeleton which can be freely traversed by macromolecules and is important for the mechanical structure and protection of the cell. It is made up of polysaccharides and carbohydrate-derived substances, which include some peptide groups. Underneath the cell wall there is the cell membrane, which appears to be the seat of the important physiological functions of assimilation and excretion. Some findings suggest that ribosomal protein synthesis is also closely associated with the membrane structure. Lipoprotein seems to be the major component or component class of the cell membranes with which we are concerned. Specimens of membrane substance have been obtained by making bacterial cells lyse through various means, preferably perhaps after the cell wall has been digested away by lysozyme, and then applying centrifugation at intermediate speeds. This results in a fraction of reproducible composition which is characterized by a high content of lipoprotein and of lipide phosphorus. The yield is variable and, unlike the procedure for wall substance, far from quantitative. Apparently substantial portions of the membrane substance are solubilized or fragmentized to a degree not accessible to intermediate speed centrifugation. Therefore, other ways had to be found for measuring in quantitative terms the membrane content in a given crop.

Our solution of this problem for the organism of our studies, Streptococcus faecalis, is based on the lipoprotein nature of the membrane. According to established procedures, the lipide moiety of lipoprotein is determined by breaking the lipide-protein linkage with boiling methanol, and then isolating the lipide component in petroleum ether. The evaporation residue of the petroleum ether extract can be weighed to give a measure of the lipide component. Besides, the petroleum ether extract can be used for phosphorus determination, and this gives a measure (colorimetric) of the lipoprotein phosphorus. We found that both lipoprotein lipide and lipide phosphorus occur only in the membrane substance—i.e., they are absent from cell wall substance as well as the cytoplasmic substance. That having been established, we could obtain reproducible quantitative values for the membrane content of different bacterial crops.

We prepared specimens of the membrane fraction from each cell type and determined two parameters: the lipide content gravimetrically, and the lipide phosphorus colorimetrically (Table I). The lipide phosphorus is in all three cases of the order of 3% of the lipide. Then we determined the same two parameters, lipide gravimetrically and lipide phosphorus colorimetrically, on the whole cell substance. Again the lipide phosphorus is of the order of 3% of the lipide. If both parameters belong exclusively to the membrane substance, membrane percentage can be calculated independently by means of the two parame-

Table I. Lipide and Lipide Phosphorus in Different Cell Products

Cell Type	Log	Val	Thr
Lipide			
% of membrane	28.3	40.2	36.0
% of cell	4.93	10.96	4.22
Membrane, % of cell calcd.	17.4	27.3	11.7
Lipide Phosphorus			
% of membrane	0.85	1.17	1.00
% of cell	0.151	0.331	0.111
Membrane, % of cell calcd.	17.8	26.6	11.1

Table II. Estimated Composition of Three Cell Types

Fraction	100-Mg. Log Cells, %	145-Mg. Val Cells, %	190-Mg. Thr Cells, %
Wall	25.5	38.0	44.0
Membrane	17.6	27.0	11.4
Cytoplasmic protein	30.5	13.4	16.5
RNA	30.2	23.8	20.0
DNA	2.84	2.18	4.05

ters. We see that, indeed, we have reasonable agreement and, more interestingly perhaps, that the three culture types vary greatly in the amount of membrane substance which they contain.

Table II shows the changes in the composition of the bacterial substance which occur when 100 mg. of log cells at the depletion point grow into valine cells (if that is the limiting amino acid), or into threonine cells if threonine is limited. The amounts formed from 100 mg. at the point of depletion average 145 mg. in the case of valine and 190 mg. in the case of threonine. The determination of wall substance by mechanical disruption and the determination of membrane substance by lipide analysis have been outlined. The other data are obtained by way of conventional procedures: DNA (deoxyribonucleic acid) by diphenylamine, and completely independently by thymine; RNA (ribonucleic acid) by ultraviolet extinction; and cytoplasmic protein from nitrogen determinations corrected for the nitrogen content of the other components.

It is important to remember that the data in Table II are percentage values. For instance, since the weight of a culture nearly doubles in the case of threonine depletion, the 25 mg. of wall substance present at the depletion point will increase to more than 80 mg., or more than threefold, in the threonine depletion cells. Similarly, in the case of DNA, 2.8 mg. of DNA at the depletion point will increase to about 8 mg. or about threefold in the threonine cells, while in the valine cells—where the total mass goes from 100 to 145 mg.—the total amount of DNA remains nearly constant. Therefore, to see what actually happens during the postexponential events, the values in the valine column have to be multiplied by 1.45, and the values in the threonine column by 1.9.

The results are shown diagramatically in Figure 5. The left bar shows the analytical breakdown of 100 mg. of exponential cell substance. Protein of the cytoplasm is shown in white and the area corresponding to the protein moiety of the membrane lipoprotein is marked by vertical dashed lines. The sum of these two protein fractions is nearly the same in all three instances. This is to be expected, since the total amount of bacterial protein cannot increase further after one of the protein-essential nutrients has been used up. The left bar shows the calculated composition of an exponentially growing culture at the depletion point, whether the depleted nutrient is valine, threonine, or any other nutrient. The center bar shows the total amount of bacterial

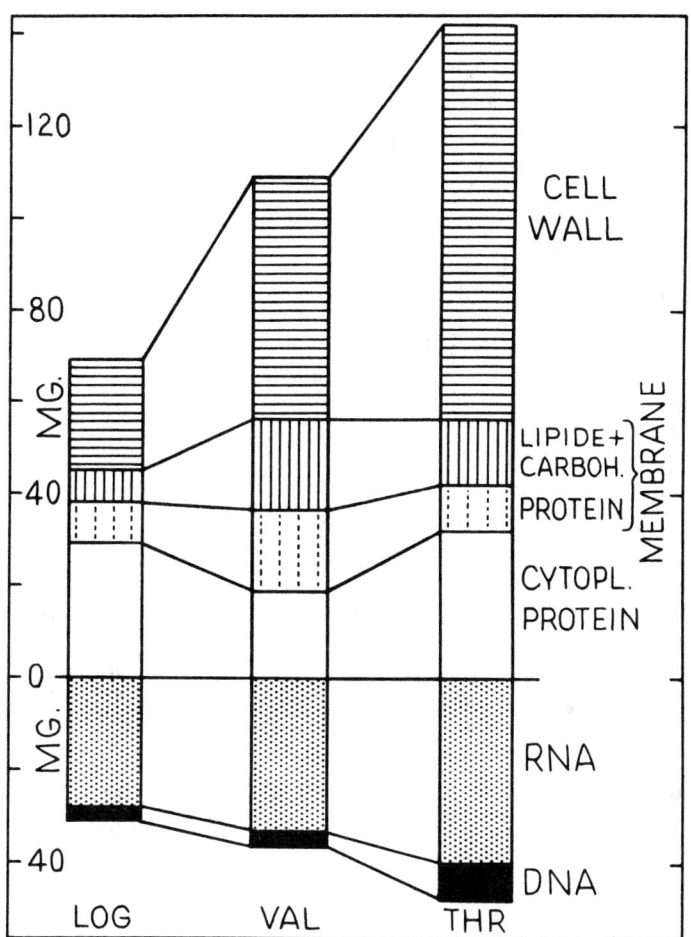

Figure 5. Pattern of changes on conversion of exponential cells into valine- or threonine- depletion cells

substance which exists when the growth which follows depletion of valine has reached the maximum. As shown in Table II, this represents a net gain of about 45%. Similarly, the last bar shows the outcome after depletion of threonine, with a net weight gain of about 90%. The horizontally shaded section represents cell wall substance. The vertically shaded section, including the dashed portion, represents membrane substance; cytoplasmic protein is shown white, RNA by a dotted area, and DNA by a black area.

Cell wall shows the greatest increase in the threonine-depletion cells. However, membrane substance increases more in the valine-depletion culture than in the threonine-depletion culture. While total protein is essentially constant, it seems necessary to assume that when

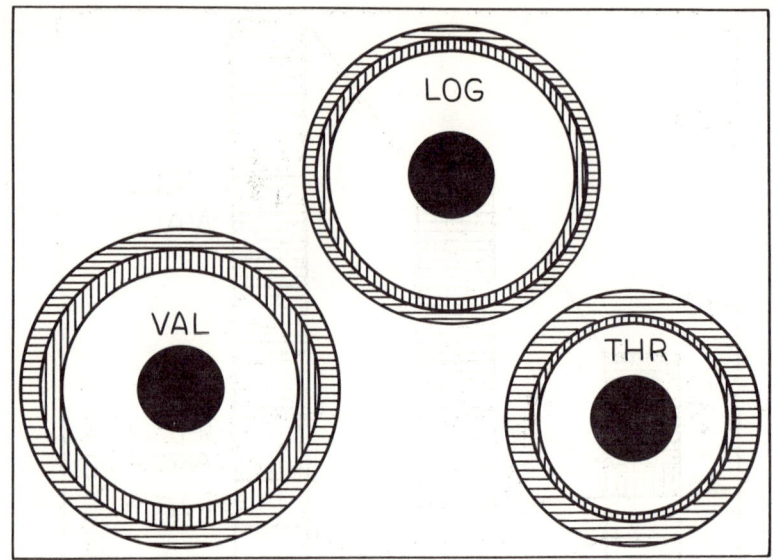

Figure 6. Cross sections of ideal spherical cells, calculated from data of Figure 5

Cell wall symbolized by horizontal shading, cytoplasmic membrane by vertical shading, cytoplasm shown in white, and DNA in black

exponential cells are converted into valine-depletion cells this entails a conversion of some cytoplasmic protein to lipoprotein of the membrane. RNA increases to some extent, but more interesting is what happens to DNA. There is a minor increase in the valine cells, but in the threonine cells there is about three times as much DNA as was present at the point of depletion when net protein synthesis ceased.

These are the facts within our experimental limits of accuracy. The remainder is speculation, utilizing two reasonably well supported assumptions. One is the principle, proposed by the Vendrelys, that for a given species the amount of DNA per cell remains constant. The other is the simple assumption that the cellular unit of a streptococcus is essentially spherical. On the basis of the principle of constant DNA, calculation indicates that the cell number has increased by about 10% in the formation of valine cells, but has tripled in the formation of threonine cells, since there is three times as much DNA as at the depletion point. This means that the average valine cell weighs about one third more than the exponential cell: If 100 corresponds to one exponential cell and 145 corresponds to about 1.1 valine cells, the cellular unit corresponds to about 130. Similarly, if the 190-mg. threonine cells represent three cells, the single threonine cell corresponds to about 65—i.e., it is about one third smaller than the exponential cell. By applying simple spherical geometry to these results one can calculate from the estimated relative spherical diameters, and from the percentage values of wall substance and of membrane substance, the thickness of the outermost wall layer and the thickness of the membrane layer just below.

The outcome of such calculations is shown graphically in Figure 6. Obviously this diagram is not only hypothetical but also schematical, and subject to qualifications and corrections. As it stands, it suggests that what we call the valine cell has a double-thickness wall and a double-thickness membrane, and is one third bigger than the exponential cell. On the other hand, the threonine cell is one third smaller than the exponential cell and it has a single-thickness membrane and a double-thickness wall.

Whether or not this is actually so, and what biochemical mechanisms effect the observed changes in bacterial composition, are matters for further research. Meanwhile, in the parlance of the geneticist, a single genotype gives rise to different phenotypes as a result of the disappearance of different single amino acids from the cellular environment, a phenomenon which may be viewed as a rudimentary form of cellular differentiation.

Acknowledgment

The author acknowledges his gratitude to his colleagues and co-workers, particularly Gerald Shockman and Joseph Kolb, who have helped to bring this work to its present stage. The work was supported by the Office of Naval Research, the National Institute of Health, and the American Cancer Society.

Literature Cited

(1) Kolb, J. J., Weidner, M. A., Toennies, G., Anal. Biochem., 5, 78 (1963).
(2) Shockman, G. D., J. Biol. Chem. 234, 2340 (1959).
(3) Shockman, G. D., Conover, M. J., Kolb, J. J., Phillips, P. M., Riley, L. S., Toennies, G., J. Bacteriol. 81, 36 (1961).
(4) Shockman, G. D., Conover, M. J., Kolb, J. J., Riley, L. S., Toennies, G., Ibid., 81, 44 (1961).
(5) Shockman, G. D., Kolb. J. J., Bakay, B., Conover, M. J., Toennies, G., Ibid., in press.
(6) Shockman, G. D., Kolb. J. J., Toennies, G., Biochim. Biophys. Acta 24, 203 85, 168 (1963).
(7) Shockman, G. D., Kolb, J. J., Toennies, G., J. Biol. Chem. 230, 961 (1958).
(8) Toennies, G., Bakay, B., Shockman, G. D., Ibid., 234, 3269 (1959).
(9) Toennies, G., Gallant, D. L., Growth 13, 7 (1949).
(10) Ibid., p. 21.
(11) Toennies, G., Gallant, D. L., J. Biol. Chem. 177, 831 (1949).
(12) Toennies., G., Iszard, L., Rogers, N. B., Shockman, G. D., J. Bacteriol. 82, 857 (1961).
(13) Toennies, G., Shockman, G. D., Arch. Biochem. Biophys. 45, 447 (1953).
(14) Toennies, G., Shockman, G. D., 6th International Congress on Biochemistry, Vol. XIII, Colloquia, Vienna, 1958.
(15) Toennies, G., Shockman, G. D., Kolb, J. J., Biochemistry, 2, 294 (1963).

Received November 30, 1962.

10
Biosynthesis and Utilization of Acetyl Phosphate, Formyl Phosphate, and Carbamyl Phosphate and their Relations to the Urea Cycle

SANTIAGO GRISOLIA AND LUISA RAIJMAN

Department of Biochemistry,
School of Medicine, University of Kansas,
Kansas City, Kan.

Animal and bacterial enzymes that utilize or synthesize carbamyl phosphate have activity with acetyl phosphate. Acyl phosphatase hydrolyzes both substrates, and may be involved in the specific dynamic action of proteins. Ornithine and aspartic transcarbamylases also synthesize acetylornithine and acetyl aspartate. Finally, bacterial carbamate kinase and animal carbamyl phosphate synthetase utilize acetyl phosphate as well as carbamyl phosphate in the synthesis of adenosine triphosphate. The synthesis of acetyl phosphate and of formyl phosphate by carbamyl phosphate synthetases is described. The mechanism of carbon dioxide activation by animal carbamyl phosphate synthetase is reviewed on the basis of the findings concerning acetate and formate activation.

This article discusses the present status of the mechanism of carbamyl phosphate (carbamyl-P) formation and illustrates that the reagents acetyl phosphate (acetyl-P) and carbamyl-P can replace each other with a number of well defined and/or highly purified enzymes.

While quite apparent to us now, it has taken many years to realize that acetyl-P and carbamyl-P could be substrates for the same enzymes. Acetyl-P was considered, for some years, an important intermediate for acetylation. However, no evidence for either its synthesis or its utilization, other than by phosphatase action (26) with animal preparations, could be demonstrated until recently. The discovery of coenzyme A and acetyl coenzyme A changed the status of this reagent from a possible intermediate to more or less a curiosity, as far as animal systems were concerned. The advances made with acetyl CoA and the fact that coenzyme A is not involved in citrulline synthesis (12) perhaps justify the delay in testing the possible substitution of acetyl-P for carbamyl-P as a substrate.

This presentation also indicates that all carbamyl-P and acetyl-P reactions thus far studied are related via the urea cycle. The newer findings and their relation to the urea cycle are outlined in Figure 1.

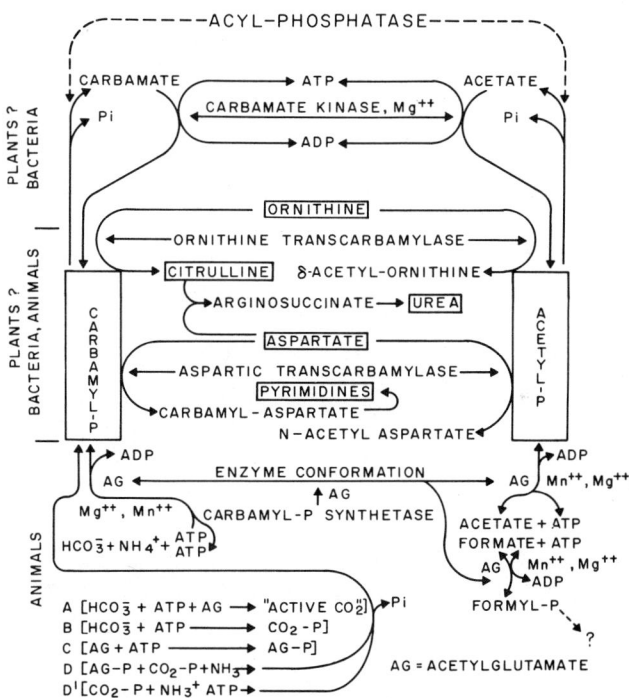

Figure 1. Interrelations of carbamyl-P, acetyl-P, and formyl-P metabolism with the urea cycle

Studies with Acyl Phosphatase

The large concentrations of acyl phosphatase present in most tissues led to the belief that it prevented the demonstration of acetyl-P biosynthesis and accumulation in animal tissues. We purified extensively, some years ago, what we first thought to be a specific carbamyl-P phosphatase. This enzyme interested us as a tool for better understanding the mechanism of citrulline synthesis; however, on testing for specificity, we found that it attacked acetyl-P just as readily as carbamyl-P.

The brain enzyme has been purified over 1000-fold and shown to be homogeneous by ultracentrifugation and electrophoresis criteria (36); the activity ratio for acetyl-P over carbamyl-P remains unchanged with purification. This enzyme is one of the smallest on record; the molecular weight from physical data is 13,200 and from amino acid analysis is 12,600; the amino acid composition of the enzyme is given in Table I. The terminal amino acid is aspartic acid (25). Cystine has not been detected.

Table I. Amino Acid Composition of Brain Acyl Phosphatase

Amino Acid	µmoles/0.78 Mg. Protein	Calculated No. of Residues [a] per Mole Protein
Lysine	0.64	13
Histidine	0.10	2
Ammonia	0.68	14
Arginine	0.20	4
Methionine sulfoxides	0.05	1 [b]
Cysteic acid	0.04	1 [c]
Aspartic acid	0.54	11
Threonine	0.38	7
Serine	0.42	8
Glutamic acid	0.82	16
Proline	0.44	9
Glycine	0.51	10
Alanine	0.43	9
1/2 cystine	0 [d]	0
Valine	0.31	6
Methionine	trace	1 [b]
Isoleucine	0.27	5
Leucine	0.32	6
Tyrosine	0.09	2
Phenylalanine	0.12	2
Tryptophan	--	(1) [e]

[a] Assuming cysteine = methionine = 1 mole/mole enzyme.
[b] Methionine sulfoxides calculated as methionine.
[c] Cysteic acid = cysteine.
[d] As little as 0.01 µmole would have been detected.
[e] Small amount of degradation product of tryptophan found. At least 1 residue tryptophan assumed to be present.

The great stability of acyl phosphatase, together with the lack of disulfide bridges, is unusual in enzyme chemistry. The high specific rotation, $-[\alpha]_D = 89.3$, is of interest also, suggesting that the enzyme does not have an appreciable number of residues in the α-helix configuration. This is consistent with the relatively large number of proline residues which, if evenly distributed, would prevent α-helix formation (7). The acyl phosphatase may play a significant role in physiological phenomena such as hibernation and specific dynamic action (4).

Heat stability and other characteristics indicate that this enzyme may be identical with the acetyl phosphatase of Lippman (26), which also catalyzes the hydrolysis of 1,3-diphosphoglycerate (21).

In spite of the indication that the same enzyme utilized carbamyl-P and acetyl-P, we did not realize the possibility, until some 4 years later, that acetyl-P could be synthesized or used for synthetic purposes in animal tissues.

Studies with Ornithine Transcarbamylase

As indicated in Reactions 1 and 2, both carbamyl-P and acetyl-P can react with ornithine to form either citrulline or δ-acetylornithine with ornithine transcarbamylase (15).

$$\text{Carbamyl-P} + \text{ornithine} \rightarrow \text{citrulline} + P_i \qquad (1)$$

$$\text{Acetyl-P} + \text{ornithine} \rightarrow \delta\text{-acetylornithine} + P_i \qquad (2)$$

While the α-amino group of ornithine could also react with acetyl-P, this possibility was eliminated in a number of ways. Chromatography in the automatic recording amino acid analyzer by the procedure of Spackman, Stein, and Moore (41) yields excellent separation of δ-acetylornithine and α-acetylornithine. Only traces of α-acetylornithine have been detected with ornithine transcarbamylase and acetyl-P; the product is always better than 95% δ-acetylornithine. The separation of α- and δ-acetylornithine by paper chromatography is not practically feasible, although both acetyl derivatives are very readily separated from ornithine (15). δ-Acetylornithine is a natural product first isolated from a Siberian plant 26 years ago (28) and now known to be present in many plants (39).

The product of the stoichiometric reaction of acetyl-P with ornithine, catalyzed by ornithine transcarbamylase, has been shown unequivocally to be δ-acetylornithine; the transcarbamylases from rat liver, frog liver, and bacteria, however, even though yielding the same product, appear to differ in their ratios of activity with carbamyl-P and acetyl-P (Table II). While it is possible that the synthesis of δ-acetylornithine is catalyzed by other enzymes (16), the different ratios may be due to species differences; we know now that the ratios of activity with carbamyl-P and acetyl-P of all ornithine transcarbamylases thus far tested remain constant with purification. Further, the ratio of citrulline to acetylornithine formation does not change with a number of treatments, such as heat inactivation of preparations containing orni-

Table II. Relative Rates of Utilization of Acetyl-P and Carbamyl-P with Animal and Bacterial Ornithine Transcarbamylases

	Rat Liver	Frog Liver	Bacteria
Carbamyl-P	34	245	900
Acetyl-P	4.1	7.4	5.4

thine transcarbamylase (15). Acetyl-P seems to be used much more effectively by animal preparations than by bacterial preparations of both ornithine transcarbamylase and aspartic transcarbamylase (see below). Lysine reacts, although very slowly, with either acetyl-P or carbamyl-P and ornithine transcarbamylase.

Studies with Aspartic Transcarbamylase

$$\text{Aspartate + carbamyl-P} \rightarrow \text{carbamyl aspartate + Pi} \qquad (3)$$

$$\text{Aspartate + acetyl-P} \rightarrow \text{N-acetyl aspartate + Pi} \qquad (4)$$

Reactions 3 and 4 indicate that with aspartic acid, aspartic transcarbamylase, and carbamyl-P or acetyl-P, either carbamyl aspartate or acetyl aspartate can be formed. Carbamyl aspartate is the first intermediate in the formation of pyrimidines, and acetyl aspartate, of unknown function, is the amino acid derivative present in the largest concentration in brain of most species (43).

Preparations of aspartate transcarbamylase from dog intestinal mucosa, rat liver, E. coli B, and E. coli 185-482 can utilize acetyl-P, although at much slower rates than carbamyl-P. The ratio of carbamyl-P to acetyl-P transfer is of the order of 20 with mammalian enzymes, and 400 with bacterial preparations (as indicated above, the ratios of carbamyl-P to acetyl-P transferring activity are also smaller with mammalian than with bacterial ornithine transcarbamylase).

The activity of the mammalian enzymes is very low, even with carbamyl-P, and it has not yet been ascertained beyond doubt that Reactions 3 and 4 are catalyzed by animal aspartic transcarbamylase. However, the specific activity for acetyl-P and carbamyl-P utilization remains constant with purification of the transcarbamylase from E. coli 185-482, suggesting that both activities are catalyzed by the same enzyme (11).

Whether acetyl-P functions in the acetylation of lysine residues of proteins—e.g., cytochrome C—or of polypeptides [suggested by Meister and Hospelhorn (31)], or in other acetylation reactions remains to be investigated. Acetylhydroxyornithine forms a large percentage of ferrichrome (9). Extracts of sonically disrupted Ustilago sphaerogena were found to contain ornithine transcarbamylase (1 mg. of protein synthesized 40 μmoles of citrulline in 15 minutes at 37° C.). The possibility that ornithine transcarbamylase may be required to acetylate N-hydroxyornithine is an attractive one. Since the fungus can also synthesize the glutaconic derivative of δ-hydroxyornithine, it is of interest to find out if the presence of transcarbamylase in this organism may be responsible for the synthesis of one or the other derivative of hydroxyornithine.

Studies with Carbamate Kinase

Carbamate kinase from strain D_{10}, group D streptococci utilizes acetyl-P for ATP synthesis (16, 17) at approximately the same rate as carbamyl-P, according to Reactions 5 and 6.

$$\text{Acetate} + \text{ATP} \xrightarrow{\text{Mg}^{+2}} \text{acetyl-P} + \text{ADP} \quad (5)$$

$$\text{Carbamate} + \text{ATP} \xrightarrow{\text{Mg}^{+2}} \text{carbamyl-P} + \text{ADP} \quad (6)$$

To test the possibility that the carbamate kinase might be identical with acetokinase in other microorganisms, three deficient E. coli mutants, R 185-823, R prototroph, and K_{12}-wt, known to have low carbamate kinase activity, were tested for acetyl-P utilization (17). Synthesis of ATP from acetyl-P occurred much faster than from carbamyl-P; the ratios of activity for acetyl-P—carbamyl-P ranged from 8 to 20; on the other hand, the enzyme from streptococcus D_{10} utilizes carbamyl-P twice as fast as acetyl-P; this activity ratio remained unchanged throughout a 40-fold purification of the enzyme (17).

It appears then that although a number of enzymes that utilize or synthesize carbamyl-P can also utilize or synthesize acetyl-P, it cannot be assumed that all acetyl-P enzymes are also able to use carbamyl-P (11).

Studies with Carbamyl-P Synthetase

For many years we have been interested in the mechanism of citrulline synthesis from ornithine. The mechanism of the reaction was clarified considerably by Jones, Spector, and Lipmann, when they synthesized carbamyl-P chemically (24) and suggested that the material which we had first isolated from animal preparations (19) was carbamyl-P.

Acetyl Glutamate-Induced Activation and Inactivation of Carbamyl-P Synthetase

The investigation of the mechanism of action of carbamyl-P synthetase has been always associated with the study of the role of acetyl glutamate or related cofactors in the reaction:

$$\text{HCO}_3^- + \text{NH}_4^+ + 2 \text{ ATP} \xrightarrow{\text{acetyl glutamate}} \text{carbamyl-P} + 2 \text{ ADP} + \text{Pi} \quad (7)$$

In extension of previous observations from this laboratory (20) Metzenberg, Marshall, and Cohen (32) demonstrated that the frog liver carbamyl-P synthetase can be activated by preincubation with acetyl glutamate. The activation phenomenon has been extensively studied in our laboratory.

The activation is not immediate; under the conditions of Table III, nearly maximal effect was obtained in 2 minutes.

Samples containing 0.8 mg. of carbamyl-P synthetase (35), 50

Table III. Effect of Length of Preincubation on Activation of Frog
Liver Carbamyl-P Synthetase by Acetyl Glutamate. (37)

Preincubation Time, Minutes	Acetyl Glutamate Present during Preincubation	
	−	+
	Citrulline Synthesis, µmoles	
2	0.021	0.142
5	0.021	0.149
10	0.021	0.153

µmoles of Tris-Cl⁻, pH 7.4, and 2 µmoles of acetyl glutamate were preincubated at 38° for the indicated length of time. The tubes were then cooled. Incubations for the assay of carbamyl-P synthetase were conducted in a volume of 2 ml. The final concentration of reagents was: ATP, 0.004M; $KHCO_3$, 0.05M; NH_4Cl, 0.025M; $MgSO_4$, 0.01M; acetyl glutamate, 0.005M; ornithine transcarbamylase, 25 units (4); ornithine, 0.005M; Tris-Cl⁻, pH 7.4, 0.05M; and the enzyme. When any of the above reagents was present in preincubation mixtures, further additions were adjusted to temperature and to yield the indicated final concentrations during the assay. Incubation was for 1 minute at 25°. Citrulline was measured as previously described (4).

This relatively rapid type of activation explains the autocatalytic curves obtained when initial rates of citrulline synthesis are compared with those obtained after several minutes' incubation. Table IV demonstrates that by increasing the acetyl glutamate concentration and the length of incubation for the over-all synthesis, the activation was obscured. This is why the activation effect remained undetected until extremely short incubation times and low temperatures were used. Bringing a complicated reaction mixture to incubation temperature, waiting for equilibration, and completing with a last component, as is often done, may obscure effects such as the ones described here.

Table IV. Initial Rate of Synthesis of Preincubated and Unmodified Frog Liver
Carbamyl-P Synthetase at Different Concentrations of Acetyl Glutamate (37)

Incubation Time, Seconds	µmoles of Acetyl Glutamate Added					
	2		10		40	
	Exptl.	Control[a]	Exptl.	Control[a]	Exptl.	Control[a]
	µmoles Citrulline Synthesized					
12	0.13	0.01	0.17	0.02	0.17	0.03
30	0.34	0.02	0.41	0.07	0.51	0.22
60	0.77	0.16	0.94	0.34	1.03	0.72
120	1.38	0.39	1.60	0.94		
240	2.46	1.22	2.69	2.14		

[a] Control tubes contained no acetyl glutamate during preincubation period; indicated amount of this cofactor added prior to final incubation.

In the experiments of Table IV 3.2 mg. of protein from frog liver preparations (35), 100 μmoles of Tris-Cl⁻ at pH 7.4, and the indicated amount of acetyl glutamate, in a volume of 1 ml., were preincubated at 38° for 5 minutes. The tubes were cooled to 25° and completed, at definite intervals, with the components and concentration of reagents indicated in Table III, and then incubated at 25° for the indicated length of time.

The activation of the extremely unstable rat liver enzyme is less marked than that of the frog liver enzyme and is thus more difficult to demonstrate. However, as illustrated in Table V, with the aid of $C^{14}O_2$

Table V. Effect of Preincubation of Rat Liver Carbamyl-P Synthetase with Acetyl Glutamate, ATP, Mg^{+2} and HCO_3^-. (37)

Reagents Present during Preincubation	Total Counts per Minute	Calculated CO_2 Fixation, Mμmoles
None	143	6.4 (12.3)[a]
Acetyl Glutamate	549	24.4 (37.5)
Acetyl Glutamate + ATP + Mg^{+2}	1890	84 (129)

[a] Figures in parenthesis correspond to experiments where incubation time was extended to 6 seconds.

and very short incubation time, it was possible to demonstrate that the rat liver enzyme was also activated by acetyl glutamate.

In the experiments of Table V 4.5 mg. of protein from an acetone powder of rat liver mitochondria (4) containing 100 μmoles of Tris-Cl⁻ at pH 7.4, were preincubated at 25°, for 10 minutes, with the following in a volume of 1 ml.: acetyl glutamate, 5 μmoles; ATP, 4 μmoles; $MgSO_4$, 10 μmoles; and $HC^{14}O_3^-$, 100 μmoles (containing 50 μcuries). The tubes were completed at definite intervals with the components and concentration of reagents indicated in Table III, except that $HC^{14}O_3^-$ was used. The completed tubes were incubated at 25° for 3 seconds. Radioactivity was determined in aliquots from the deproteinized supernatant fluids.

Effect of Acetyl Glutamate Concentration

The degree of activation is a function of the concentration of acetyl glutamate, as shown in Figure 2. The maximal effect occurs at 2 to 5×10^{-3} M acetyl glutamate; the concentration of enzyme in these experiments was approximately 4×10^{-6} M, 1×10^{-5} M, and 2.2×10^{-5} M for curves I, II, and III, respectively. Half-maximal activation occurs at approximately 5×10^{-4} M acetyl glutamate, a value very close to the K_m for the over-all reaction, and for the acetyl glutamate-induced inactivation. The significance of this finding was pointed out by Caravaca and Grisolia (4). Similar findings with other enzymes (1, 14) indicate

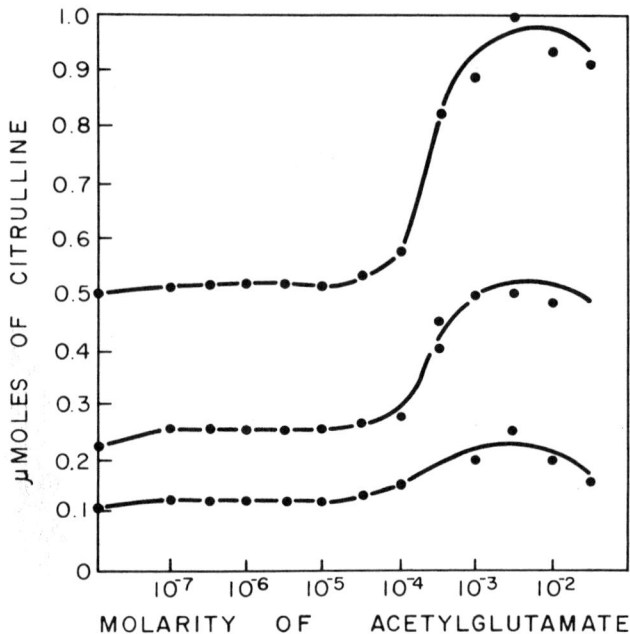

Figure 2. Dependence of activation phenomenon on concentration of acetyl glutamate

1.45, 3.45, and 7.1 mg. of frog liver enzyme (bottom, middle, and top curves, respectively) in 0.1M Tris-Cl$^-$, pH 7.4, preincubated with acetyl glutamate at indicated molarities, at 38° for 10 minutes. Tubes cooled to 25°, completed at definite intervals, and assayed under conditions of Table III. Incubation at 25°, 1 minute

the usefulness of the technique of substrate and cofactor-induced inactivation.

We have shown that there is good agreement between dissociation constants obtained by kinetic studies, and by measurements of the substrate-induced enzyme inactivation (4); the latter may yield true equilibrium constants, as is the case for K_I determinations, free from kinetic variables that may be present in estimations of Km (6). However, the constants determined by inducing inactivations cannot be accepted without properly evaluating other factors (14).

Influence of pH on Activation. The pH dependence of the activation phenomenon is illustrated in Figure 3. The fact that the activation began to appear at pH 5.6, became maximal at pH near 7.4, and remained maximal at pH as high as 10.0, indicated that a certain ionic species of acetyl glutamate might be involved in the activation of the enzyme. Since the amino group of glutamate becomes more acidic on acetylation than on carbamylation, and since both acetyl and carbamyl glutamate

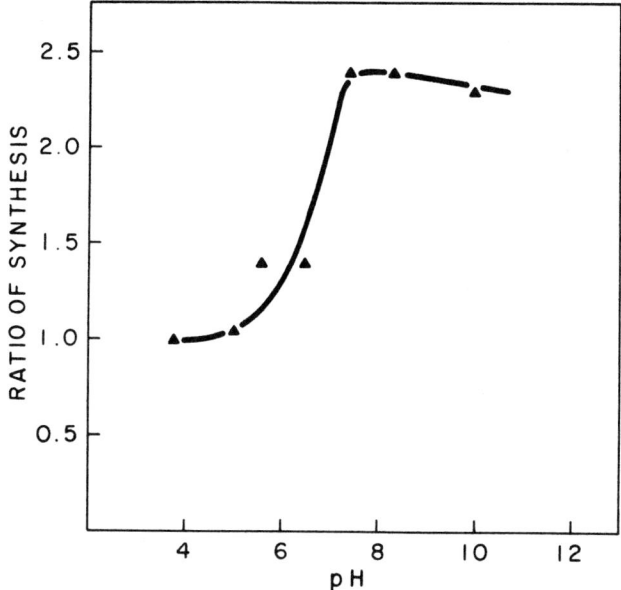

Figure 3. Influence of pH on activation of frog liver carbamyl-P synthetase by acetyl glutamate

pH adjusted with following buffers: K acetate at pH 3.8 to 5.6; K citrate at pH 6.5; Tris-Cl⁻ at pH 7.4 and 8.3; glycine at pH 10.0. Each tube contained 30 μmoles of indicated buffer, 5 μmoles of acetyl glutamate, and 1.6 mg. of enzyme protein (35). Mixtures, in volume of 1 ml., preincubated at 38° for 10 minutes; controls without acetyl glutamate carried in same manner. After cooling to 25°, additions made as in Table III (except that Tris-Cl⁻ concentration was 0.1M) and mixtures were incubated at 25°, for 1 minute. Ratios of synthesis by activated and control enzyme plotted against pH during preincubation

activate the synthetase, the species resulting from the ionization of substituent groups in carbon 2 (which occurs at different pH for acetyl and carbamyl glutamate) appears unlikely to be responsible for the activation; the ionization of the ω-carboxyl group would seem to be required. N-formyl, N-carbamyl, and N-acetyl glutamine cannot replace N-formyl, N-carbamyl, and N-acetyl glutamate in citrulline synthesis (10, 13). The effect of pH on the activation, however, may be due as well to the ionization of groups within the enzyme molecule, in which case the above-mentioned possibility may not apply.

Effect of Temperature on Activation. The extent of activation is a function of temperature; as shown in Figure 4, a linear relationship is disclosed when log K_T is plotted against $1/T$, but it is not yet known

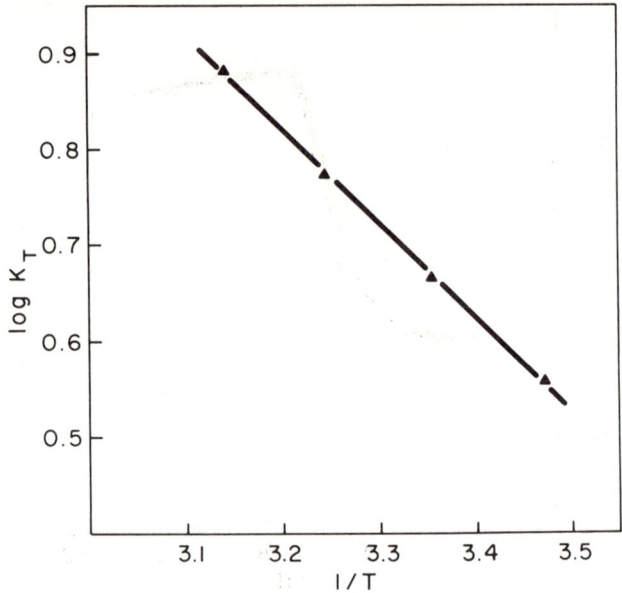

Figure 4. Effect of temperature on activation

2 mg. of frog liver carbamyl-P synthetase (35) containing 50 μmoles of Tris-Cl⁻, pH 7.4, and 5 μmoles of acetyl glutamate, in 1 ml., preincubated at 15°, 25°, 35°, 45°, for 10 minutes. Tubes rapidly taken to 25°, and completed with necessary reagents, as in Table III. Incubated at 25°, for 1 minute

whether the van't Hoff or the Arrhenius expressions apply. While the activation phenomenon occurred rapidly (see above), and full activation was reached in 10 minutes at the temperatures shown in Figure 4, that length of time was not sufficient when samples were preincubated at 5°. Once the maximal activation for a certain temperature had been reached, further activation could be obtained by a rise in temperature, but only to the level that would have been reached by initially preincubating at the higher temperature—for example, under the conditions of Figure 4, the same value was obtained when samples were first incubated at 15° and subsequently at 35°, as when preincubated at 35° only.

Once the activation had taken place, lowering the temperature did not result in a decrease to a lower level of activation. On the other hand, temperatures below 10° might result in cold inactivation.

Cold Lability of Carbamyl-P Synthetase. The acetyl glutamate-activated enzyme is less stable at low temperatures than the nonactivated enzyme preparations (35). The frog enzyme is stable over a wide temperature range. In the presence of acetyl glutamate, it retains its stability if stored above 10° and as high as 45°, but it is inactivated at 0 to 5°. This is one of four cases known to us, of enzymatically active

Table VI. Effect of Storage at 0° and of Freezing and Thawing on Stability of Frog Liver Carbamyl-P Synthetase, with and without Acetyl Glutamate (37)

Storage Time, Hours	Acetyl Glutamate Present during Storage			
	None		1×10^{-2} M	
	Citrulline Synthesis, μmoles			
0	0.32	0.30 [a]	0.54	0.52 [a]
3.5	0.33	0.30 [a]	0.28	0.24 [a]
5.5	0.31 [b]	0.28 [a]	0.15 [b]	0.09 [a]
7.5	0.33	0.28 [a]	0.13	0.09 [a]
26.5	0.33		0.02	

[a] Values attained after freezing and thawing preparation immediately before assaying.
[b] Same values obtained after reincubating enzyme at 38°, for 5 minutes, immediately before assaying.

proteins that are more stable at higher temperatures, but the only one induced by a cofactor. As further illustrated in Table VI, the acetyl glutamate-induced cold inactivation was little affected by rewarming or by freezing and thawing before assaying.

Samples containing 2 mg. of carbamyl-P synthetase (35) per ml. in 0.05M Tris-Cl⁻ at pH 7.4, and the indicated addition were preincubated at 38° for 5 minutes, cooled, and stored at 0°. Then 1.0-ml. portions were withdrawn, completed with the other necessary reagents as outlined in Table III, and incubated at 38° for exactly 1 minute.

The prompt removal of acetyl glutamate from the preincubation mixtures, by dialysis at room temperature or by precipitation of the protein with ammonium sulfate, prevented the cold inactivation. The presence of ammonium sulfate, in concentrations as high as 0.17M, did not protect the enzyme against cold inactivation (at higher molarities of the salt, precipitation began to occur). Once the cold inactivation had taken place, the enzymatic activity could not be restored either by precipitation with ammonium sulfate, or by reincubation with acetyl glutamate or with ATP and Mg^{+2}.

Upon ultracentrifugation, the unmodified enzyme shows a peak having an S_{20w} of 12×10^{-13}. In the presence of acetyl glutamate and after storage at 4° for 48 hours, the main peak separates into two components, one of which sediments at the same rate as the original peak, the other one more slowly (Figure 5). The change, however, does not parallel the changes in activity: There is no alteration of the original sedimentation pattern after 24 hours of storage in the cold, while the enzymatic activity is completely lost in the same period of time. In no case was there an appreciable precipitation of protein, not even after protracted storage.

Determination of –SH Groups in Frog Liver Carbamyl-P Synthetase. Sulfhydryl groups were measured in samples of carbamyl-P syn-

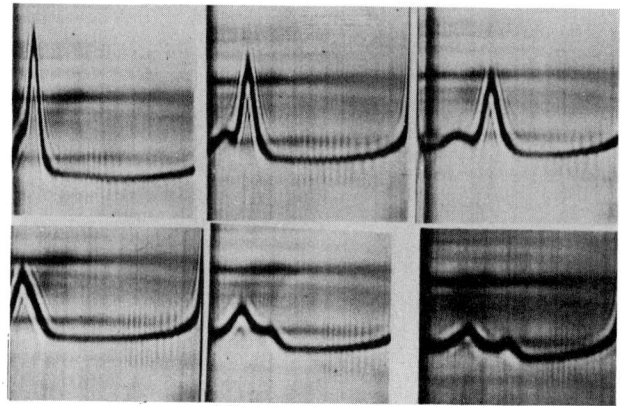

Figure 5. Ultracentrifugal pattern of frog liver carbamyl-P synthetase, before and after cold inactivation

*Top. Sedimentation pattern (left to right) of frog liver carbamyl-P synthetase (35) containing 5.5 mg. of protein per ml. after incubation at 38°, for 5 minutes
Bottom. Same preparation made 0.01M in acetyl glutamate, incubated at 38° for 5 minutes, and stored at 0° for 48 hours
Centrifugations carried out in Spinco Model E ultracentrifuge, at a speed of 52,640 r.p.m. Photographs taken at 16-minute intervals, and at bar angle of 40°*

thetase with and without acetyl glutamate activation, and before and after cold inactivation.

Photometric determinations with p-chloromercuribenzoate (3) were carried out in phosphate at pH 8; 27 ± 1 SH groups were found per mole of unmodified and also of acetyl glutamate-activated carbamyl-P synthetase. With cold-inactivated enzyme, however, only 19 to 20 groups could be detected. The same results were obtained by amperometric titration in aqueous solution (2) and in 8M urea (5); after sulfitolysis on the cold-inactivated enzyme, an average of 23 SH groups per mole of enzyme was determined. The cases thus far examined, of substrate-induced enzyme inactivation, show also a change in SH group content (1, 14).

At pH 7 (the method describes determinations at pH 5 and 7) protein began to precipitate after 15 to 20 minutes' incubation with p-chloromercuribenzoate, turning the procedure impracticable. The enzyme preparations used in our work had been lyophilized and stored for variable lengths of time; their specific activity had not decreased with storage. As the preparations were about 85% pure, a systematic error is present in our determinations. Marshall, Metzenberg, and Cohen (30) have reported that "the reaction of the enzyme with hydroxymercuribenzoate was complete in approximately 80 minutes with the concentration of reagents which were used. Between 41 and 44 moles of SH groups reacted. This value was somewhat lower for a preparation of the enzyme which had been stored for a few weeks." While the number of SH groups reported here may have to be revised, the induction of changes in the protein structure by incubation with acetyl glutamate is clearly reflected by the decrease in titratable SH groups.

Other Physical Measurements. Viscosity measurements did not show differences between samples treated with acetyl glutamate and controls, before and after storage in the cold (35). Extensive series of ultracentrifuge measurements did not clarify the phenomenon; the latter studies were conducted at several protein and acetyl glutamate concentrations, and at temperatures varying from 5° to 20°; only after cold inactivation for 40 hours were marked changes noticeable.

Rotatory power measurements were carried out and, as shown in Figure 6, enzyme preparations had an abnormal dispersion curve, that

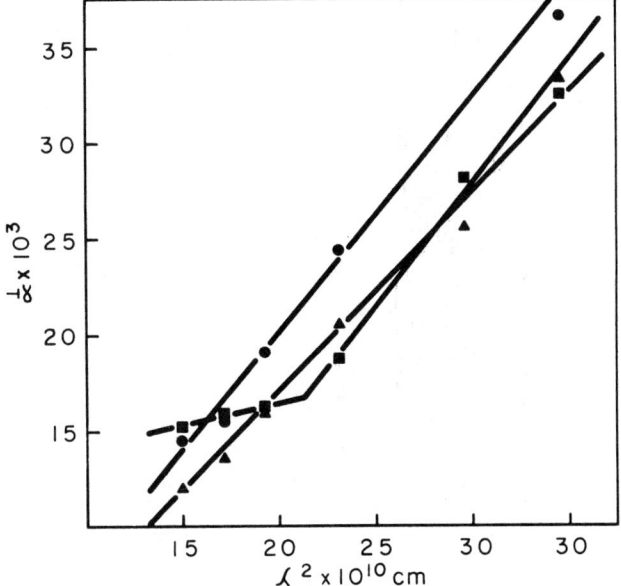

Figure 6. Optical rotatory dispersion of frog liver carbamyl-P synthetase

Solutions contained 2.2 mg. of enzyme (35) per ml.

□ *Enzyme*
△ *Enzyme in 0.005M acetyl glutamate*
○ *Enzyme in 0.005M acetyl glutamate after cold inactivation*

became linear in the presence of acetyl glutamate. After cold-inactivating, the rotatory dispersion plot remained linear, although there was a decrease in magnitude of the α values.

The addition of 1×10^{-3} M acetyl glutamate to frog liver enzyme preparation causes a 10% and immediate increase in fluorescence. This effect has been confirmed by Edelhoch (8), who concurs in our interpretation that this finding signifies acetyl glutamate-induced conformational changes of carbamyl-P synthetase. We believe that the decrease in stability induced by substrates and cofactors is, whenever it is found to occur, the simplest and most sensitive method available for the detection and study of conformational changes in enzymic proteins.

With the aid of the technique of equilibrium dialysis, Marshall, Metzenberg, and Cohen concluded recently (30) that acetyl glutamate binds to the enzyme. Binding studies with acetyl glutamate present difficulties due, for example, to the relatively high molecular weight of the enzyme, and its fairly low affinity for acetyl glutamate.

The difference in radioactivity between the protein and dialyzing compartments was used as a measure of bound acetyl glutamate (30); in one case, for example, it was determined that 100 counts had bound, with a standard deviation of ±20. It appears that a statistically significant number of experiments is required to ascertain the binding of acetyl glutamate, in view of the small magnitudes and large experimental errors involved.

Acetyl glutamate may participate in the synthesis of a precursor of carbamyl-P, in a manner as yet hypothetical; it doubtlessly causes a deep alteration of the enzyme structure, and that may be in fact its sole involvement in the over-all reaction.

Since only after cold inactivation was there any difference in sedimentation (see above) and particularly in SH content, substrate-induced cold inactivation may be related to the general phenomenon of substrate-induced inactivation (18).

The data in Table V show that the addition of ATP and Mg^{+2} increases the activation by acetyl glutamate of rat liver carbamyl-P synthetase. The same is true of the frog liver enzyme, although the superimposed ATP activation is less marked in this case. Perhaps the acetyl glutamate–induced and the acetyl glutamate-ATP-Mg^{+2}–induced activations are additive phenomena. ATP and Mg^{+2} do not activate either synthetase, in a strict sense, in the absence of acetyl glutamate. The possibility that the activation by acetyl glutamate might be related to the presence of trace amounts of ATP was eliminated for both the rat and frog liver enzymes, in experiments in which the enzymes were preincubated with glucose and hexokinase prior to the addition of acetyl glutamate.

Studies with Acetyl-P and Formyl-P

It was found in our laboratories that acetyl-P (16, 33, 38) and formyl-P can be utilized for the synthesis of ATP with carbamyl-P synthetase from both rat and frog liver. These reactions resemble the Reaction 8 (13) for ATP synthesis from carbamyl-P.

$$\text{"CO}_2\text{ intermediate"} + \text{ATP} + \text{NH}_3 \xrightleftharpoons{\text{acetyl glutamate}} \text{carbamyl-P} + \text{ADP} \qquad (8)$$

Acetyl-P and formyl-P were recently synthesized by the carbamyl-P synthetase in our laboratories; some of the characteristics of these reactions may help in the clarification of the mechanism of action of carbamyl-P synthetase.

A considerable amount of acetyl or formyl phosphate is synthesized in the absence of acetyl glutamate.

Coenzyme A does not appear to be involved, since the passage of the enzyme preparation through a Dowex-2 column, or the addition of coenzyme A to the incubation mixtures, does not change the velocity of the reaction. Coenzyme A is not involved in citrulline synthesis (13).

These unpublished findings of the writers indicate that acetyl glutamate is not an absolute requirement for the synthesis of acetyl-P or formyl-P, and they render unlikely the possibility that an acetic or formic acid derivative of acetyl glutamate may be involved. The new findings are represented by Reactions 9 and 10.

$$\text{Formate} + \text{ATP} \xrightleftharpoons[\text{Mg}^{+2}, \text{Mn}^{+2}, \text{ acetyl glutamate}]{\text{Mn}^{+2}, \text{Mg}^{+2}; \text{ acetyl glutamate stimulates}} \text{formyl-P} + \text{ADP} \qquad (9)$$

$$\text{Acetate} + \text{ATP} \xrightleftharpoons[\text{Mg}^{+2}, \text{Mn}^{+2}, \text{ acetyl glutamate}]{\text{Mn}^{+2}, \text{Mg}^{+2}; \text{ acetyl glutamate stimulates}} \text{acetyl-P} + \text{ADP} \qquad (10)$$

The possibility that enzymes other than carbamyl-P synthetase might be responsible for Reactions 9 and 10, although unlikely, was considered. The frog liver carbamyl-P synthetase shows equal thermal stability for both carbamyl-P synthesis and for ATP synthesis from acetyl-P in the absence and presence of acetyl glutamate (33); further, the ratio of activity for Reactions 9 and 10 to that of the over-all synthesis of carbamyl-P (Reactions 11 and 8) remained unchanged with purification.

Incorporation of $HC^{14}O_3^-$. Frog liver carbamyl-P synthetase incorporates $HC^{14}O_3^-$ when incubated with ATP and Mg^{+2} (Table VII); incubation with acetyl glutamate alone does not result in the fixation of $C^{14}O_2$ into a stable intermediate, but the addition of acetyl glutamate to ATP and Mg^{+2} increases the total fixation. This represents an apparent contradiction to the statement previously made, that neither the rat nor the frog liver enzymes are activated by ATP and Mg^{+2} alone. The contradiction is only apparent, however; it can be seen in Table VII that the total incorporation in these experiments, after 10-minute incubations, amounts to 10 to 100 mμmoles of bicarbonate; the incorporation would not be apparent under the conditions used in the study of the activation phenomenon.

Table VII. Incorporation of $C^{14}O_2$ with Frog Liver Carbamyl-P Synthetase (37)

Reagents Present during Incubation	Total Counts per Minute	CO_2 Fixation, Mμmoles
$HC^{14}O_3^-$	266	9.6
$HC^{14}O_3^-$ + acetyl glutamate	177 [a]	6.4 [a]
$HC^{14}O_3^-$ + ATP + Mg^{+2}	3,161	114
$HC^{14}O_3^-$ + acetyl glutamate + ATP + Mg^{+2}	5,366	193
$HC^{14}O_3^-$ + acetyl glutamate + ATP + Mg^{+2} + NH_4^+	22,290	802
$HC^{14}O_3^-$, zero time	262	9.4

[a] Incorporation of $HC^{14}O_3^-$ by enzyme with acetyl glutamate was consistently lower than that of mixtures containing enzyme and bicarbonate only.

In the experiments reported in Table VII 4 mg. of protein from frog liver preparations (35) were incubated with the following, when indicated: Tris-Cl$^-$, pH 7.4, 50 μmoles; acetyl glutamate, 5 μmoles; ATP, 4 μmoles; $MgSO_4$, 10 μmoles; NH_4Cl, 100 μmoles; $HC^{14}O_3^-$, 100 μmoles (containing 50 μcuries). Incubations were at 38°, for 10 minutes, in a volume of 1 ml. Protein was precipitated with 1 ml. of 1M $HClO_4$, and N_2 was passed through the solutions. After centrifugation, 0.1 ml. of the supernatant fluids was neutralized, plated, and counted.

Cold-inactivated frog liver carbamyl-P synthetase is still capable of incorporating $HC^{14}O_3^-$ when incubated with ATP and Mg^{+2}.

The possible role of biotin in the synthesis of carbamyl-P was reinvestigated (27). The addition of biotin to crude rat liver enzyme resulted, in one series of experiments, in increased synthesis, ranging from 21 to 53% over the control level. This effect could not be reproduced with crude or purified preparations. The activity of frog liver enzyme is also unaffected by biotin at any stage of purification.

Avidin inhibits carbamyl-P synthesis by rat liver enzyme (10 units cause a 40 to 70% inhibition, depending on the purity of the enzyme), but does not affect the frog liver preparations. Preincubation of the avidin with a large excess of biotin does not prevent the inhibition of the mammalian enzyme, suggesting that the effect is not strictly due to the biotin-binding capacity of avidin. We concluded that biotin is not directly involved in the synthesis of carbamyl-P, although the enzyme may contain bound biotin. Also, this vitamin may play a role in enzyme synthesis (34).

Mechanism of Carbamyl-P Synthetase

Since the discovery of the catalytic action of acetyl glutamate and related reagents, it has been repeatedly proposed by several workers (19, 23, 32) that the synthesis of carbamyl-P by carbamyl-P synthetase proceeds stepwise.

The possibility that more than one enzyme is involved in the synthesis of carbamyl-P has been considered, and cannot as yet be entirely dismissed; however, immunological studies with highly purified frog and rat liver preparations (29) fully justify the assumption that only one enzyme, perhaps multiheaded, is responsible for the reaction. We have suggested (35) that two related phenomena are involved in the complicated acetyl glutamate requirement of carbamyl-P synthetase for carbamyl-P synthesis: one inflicting structural changes in the enzyme protein; another, requiring ATP, resulting in the accumulation of an intermediate.

Grisolia and Towne (20) first proposed that an intermediate was formed prior to the synthesis of carbamyl-P. The idea of an intermediate was further strengthened by later evidence (35) regarding the increase in synthetic activity that follows the preincubation of the rat liver enzyme with acetyl glutamate, ATP, and Mg^{+2}, and by the demonstration that, after preincubation of the enzyme with acetyl glutamate, ATP, Mg^{+2}, and HCO_3^-, followed by the removal of ATP from the incubation mixtures, some citrulline was still synthesized upon addition of ornithine and ornithine transcarbamylase.

Metzenberg, Marshall, and Cohen (32) proposed the following scheme for the incorporation of CO_2 into carbamyl-P:

$$ATP + CO_2 \xrightarrow{\text{acetyl glutamate}} ADP + Pi + \text{"active } CO_2\text{"} \quad (11)$$

$$ATP + \text{"active } CO_2\text{"} + NH_3 \xrightleftharpoons{\text{acetyl glutamate}} ADP + \text{carbamyl-P} \quad (8)$$

Evidence pointing to this mechanism included the increased utilization of ATP with decreased carbamyl-P synthesis induced by cobalt ions (32); the utilization of ATP by the enzyme in the absence of ammonia, a phenomenon enhanced by Mn^{+2} (32); and the phosphatase-like effect of hydroxylamine, extensively studied by Caravaca and Grisolia (4). [No evidence of the possible formation of a hydroxamate was obtained (4).] The same data indicate that ammonia enters the reaction last, releasing the hypothetical intermediate with simultaneous formation of carbamyl-P.

The partial reversibility of the reaction is also an argument in favor of the stepwise mechanism, although the latter is not the only possible explanation; 2 moles of ATP are utilized per mole of carbamyl-P synthesized (Reactions 11 and 8), yet only 1 mole of ATP can be synthesized from 1 mole of carbamyl-P. It has been thought that the synthesis of ATP from carbamyl-P reflected a reversal of Reaction 8, while Reaction 11 was assumed irreversible. The activation reactions of acetate and formate are perhaps identical with Reaction 11, and yet they are reversible, as indicated in Reactions 9 and 10. It may well be that the reverse reaction, Reaction 8—e.g., ATP synthesis from carbamyl-P—is part of Reaction 11 in all cases. This would imply that while the synthesis of carbamyl-P is a two-step process, the "activation" of HCO_3^- and the formation of ATP from carbamyl-P (in essence a reversal of CO_2 activation) may be carried out in one step.

While acetyl glutamate is required as a cofactor for the over-all synthesis of carbamyl-P, as well as for the synthesis of ATP (Reaction 8), the absolute requirement for acetyl glutamate in the postulated first step—the CO_2 activation—is still conjectural; there is, in fact, evidence to the contrary.

The role of acetyl glutamate remained undefined in Marshall's proposition (30); Jones and Spector (23) proposed a mechanism for the synthesis of carbamyl-P dependent on the hypothetical formation of carboxyl phosphate from ATP and HCO_3^-, followed by the synthesis of a carbonic acid derivative of acetyl glutamate. To our knowledge no further evidence of the existence of these intermediates has been obtained to date. The experiments performed in our laboratories on the incorporation of $HC^{14}O_3^-$ may be interpreted differently. If a carbonic acid derivative of acetyl glutamate is formed, the presence of an excess of acetyl glutamate in the incubation mixtures should favor the CO_2 fixing reaction, resulting in increased incorporation; however, the structural modifications induced by acetyl glutamate, which result in a more active form of the enzyme, would be sufficient to increase the incorporation.

To the previous data must be added the exchange experiments carried out by several investigators; most atoms of acetyl and/or carbamyl glutamate have been labeled (except those that freely equilibrate with water), and their exchangeability with other elements participating in the reaction has been tested. No indication of exchange has been found thus far. While this does not exclude the participation of acetyl glutamate in the formation of an intermediate, it limits the possibilities to a narrow group.

Since the frog liver synthetase is activated by acetyl glutamate without ATP, Marshall, Metzenberg, and Cohen (30) concluded that acetyl glutamylphosphate was not an intermediate. As shown above, the presence of ATP and Mg^{+2} together with acetyl glutamate always enhances activity (particularly in the case of the rat liver enzyme, where the activation by acetyl glutamate alone is barely demonstrable), and we have been able to reproduce the experiments where citrulline was synthesized after the removal of ATP (20). It appears then that the activation of carbamyl-P synthetase by acetyl glutamate does not necessarily exclude the possibility of a phosphorylated acetyl glutamate intermediate.

Three important distinguishing facts concerning the synthesis of acetyl-P and formyl-P will be brought to mind: (1) that unlike the synthesis of carbamyl-P, no ammonia is involved in the synthesis of acetyl-P or formyl-P; (2) that Mn^{+2} rather than Mg^{+2} is the most active cation in acetyl-P and formyl-P synthesis and in ATP synthesis from acetyl-P (while Mg^{+2} is most active in the synthesis of carbamyl-P, Mn^{+2} is again more active in the utilization of ATP by the frog liver enzyme in the absence of ammonium ions); and (3) that the stoichiometry of the reaction with respect to ATP appears to differ with the product, one ATP being utilized per mole of formyl-P synthesized (evidence indicates that the same is the case for acetyl-P synthesis).

On the basis of the evidence available to date, several hypotheses on the mechanism of synthesis of carbamyl-P may be maintained; however, they must now be applicable as well to the synthesis of acetyl and formyl-P.

In view of the new information presented with regard to the synthesis of carbamyl, acetyl, and formyl-P, two further postulations on the enzymatic mechanism may be advanced.

The "activation" of acetate, formate, and bicarbonate may be carried out by the synthetase by an analogous mechanism, conducing to the synthesis of acetyl-P, formyl-P, and an unidentified compound (perhaps carboxyl-P), respectively. The activation possibly occurs in one step, utilizing 1 mole of ATP per mole of product synthesized (Reaction 12):

$$\left.\begin{array}{l} CH_3-COO^- \\ H-COO^- \\ HCO_3^- \end{array}\right\} + ATP \rightleftharpoons \begin{array}{l} \text{acetyl-P} \\ \text{formyl-P + ADP} \\ \text{"}CO_2-P\text{"} \end{array} \qquad (12)$$

The participation of ammonia [that can apparently be replaced by O-methylhydroxylamine (30)] may be related to a second function of the enzyme, accomplished in the case of the activation of HCO_3^-, and only in that case (Reaction 13):

$$\text{"}CO_2-P\text{"} + NH_3 + ATP \rightleftharpoons \text{carbamyl-P} + ADP + Pi \qquad (13)$$

The enzyme (perhaps involving a second binding site for ATP) may complete the activation of HCO_3^- to carbamyl-P in the following manner:

$$HCO_3^- + ATP \rightarrow \text{"}CO_2-P\text{"} + ADP \qquad (14)$$

$$\text{Acetyl glutamate} + ATP \rightarrow \text{"acetyl glutamate-P"} + ADP \qquad (15)$$

$$\text{"}CO_2-P\text{"} + \text{"Acetyl glutamate-P"} + NH_3 \rightarrow$$

$$\text{carbamyl-P + acetyl glutamate + Pi} \qquad (16)$$

This mechanism is not inconsistent with the fact that the role of acetyl glutamate as a cofactor appears to be fundamentally associated with the structural changes it induces in the enzyme protein.

The findings described here and their possible interrelations with the urea cycle are presented in Figure 1.

Recent Work

Important contributions to two subjects of this paper have been made since its submission:

Stadtman has demonstrated (42) the conversion of carbamyl phosphate and acetate to acetyl phosphate, catalyzed either by a crude lysine system or by a purified acetate kinase from C. sticklandii. ADP and

Mg^{+2} were required for the reaction to proceed. The acetyl phosphate is utilized for the synthesis of acetyl-CoA, required for lysine degradation. The importance of Stadtman's finding becomes apparent upon close examination of the experimental data.

Schooler, Fahien, and Cohen (40) have reported that 2-acetoxyglutarate is an activator of carbamyl phosphate synthetase. One of the structures proposed by Jones and Spector for the carboxylated derivative of acetyl glutamate is thus ruled out.

Acknowledgment

The authors are grateful to E. Stadtman for a gift of formyl phosphate and to J. B. Neilands for Ustilago sphaerogena.

Literature Cited

(1) Amelunxen, R., Grisolia, S., J. Biol. Chem. 237, 3240 (1962).
(2) Benesch, R. E., Lardy, H. A., Benesch, R., Ibid., 216, 663 (1955).
(3) Boyer, P. D., J. Am. Chem. Soc. 76, 4331 (1954).
(4) Caravaca, J., Grisolia, S., J. Biol. Chem. 235, 684 (1960).
(5) Carter, J. R., Ibid., 234, 1705 (1959).
(6) Dixon, M., Webb, E. C., in "Enzymes," p. 373, Academic Press, New York, 1958.
(7) Doty, P., Proceedings of IVth International Congress of Biochemistry, Vol. 8, p. 8, 1958.
(8) Edelhoch, H., private communication.
(9) Emery, T., Neilands, J. B., J. Am. Chem. Soc. 83, 1626 (1961).
(10) Grassl, M., Bach, S. J., Biochim. Biophys. Acta 42, 154 (1960).
(11) Grisolia, S., Amelunxen, R., Raijman, L., Biochem. Biophys. Research Communs., 11, 75 (1963).
(12) Grisolia, S., Cohen, P. P., J. Biol. Chem. 191, 189 (1951).
(13) Ibid., 204, 753 (1953).
(14) Grisolia, S., Fernandez, M., Amelunxen, R., Quijada, C. L., Biochem. J. 85, 568 (1962).
(15) Grisolia, S., Harmon, P., Biochim. Biophys. Acta 59, 482 (1962).
(16) Grisolia, S., Harmon, P., Biochem. Biophys. Research Communs. 7, 357 (1962).
(17) Grisolia, S., Harmon, P., Raijman, L., Biochim. Biophys. Acta 62, 293 (1962).
(18) Grisolia, S., Joyce, B. K., Biochem. Pharmacol. 3, 167 (1960).
(19) Grisolia, S., Marshall, R. O., in "Symposium on Amino Acid Metabolism," W. D. McElroy and B. Glass, eds., p. 258, Johns Hopkins Press, Baltimore, 1955.
(20) Grisolia, S., Towne, J. C., Biochim. Biophys. Acta 25, 224 (1957).
(21) Harary, I., Ibid., 26, 434 (1957).
(22) Hospelhorn, V., Raijman, L., Grisolia, S., unpublished experiments.
(23) Jones, M. E., Spector, L., J. Biol. Chem. 235, 2897 (1960).
(24) Jones, M. E., Spector, L., Lipmann, F., J. Am. Chem. Soc. 77, 819 (1955).
(25) Kimmel, J., University of Utah Medical School, Salt Lake City, Utah, private communication.
(26) Lipmann, F., Advan. Enzymol. 6, 231 (1946).
(27) Macleod, P. R., Grisolia, S., Cohen, P. P., Lardy, H. A., J. Biol. Chem. 180, 1003 (1949).

(28) Manske, R. H. F., Can. J. Res. 15, 84 (1937).
(29) Marshall, M., Cohen, P. P., J. Biol. Chem. 236, 718 (1961).
(30) Marshall, M., Metzenberg, R. L., Cohen, P. P., Ibid., 236, 2229 (1961).
(31) Meister, A., Hospelhorn, V., private communication.
(32) Metzenberg, R. L., Marshall, M., Cohen, P. P., J. Biol. Chem. 233, 1560 (1958).
(33) Novoa, W. B., Grisolia, S., Ibid., 237, PC 2710 (1962).
(34) Ochoa, S., Mehler, A., Blanchard, M. L., Jukes, T. H., Hoffman, C. E., Regan, M., Ibid., 170, 413 (1947).
(35) Raijman, L., Grisolia, S., Biochem. Biophys. Res. Communs. 4, 262 (1961).
(36) Raijman, L., Grisolia, S., Edelhoch, H., J. Biol. Chem. 235, 2340 (1960).
(37) Raijman, L., Grisolia, S., unpublished experiments.
(38) Raijman, L., Grisolia, S., Novoa, W., Federation Proc. 22, 534 (1963).
(39) Reuter, G., Flora 145, 326 (1957).
(40) Schooler, J. M., Fahien, L. A., Cohen, P. P., J. Biol. Chem. 238, PC1909 (1963).
(41) Spackman, D. H., Stein, W. H., Moore, S., Anal. Chem. 30, 1190 (1958).
(42) Stadtman, Thressa, J. Biol. Chem. 238, 2766 (1963).
(43) Tallan, H. H., Moore, S., Stein, W. H., Ibid., 211, 927 (1954).

Received April 26, 1963. Work supported by U. S. Public Health grants A1855 and E3505.

INDEX

A

Accumulation capacity, extra-
    cellular osmotic activity .. 106
Acetate, effect on glutamate ac-
    cumulation. 107
  incorporation into cell wall .108, 109
  kinase 132
Acetyl phosphate, biosynthesis
    and utilization of 128
  identity 128
Acyl phosphatase, properties . . . 129
  role in dynamic action 130
Ala-thr ratios 6
Albumin 8, 20
Alanine. 58, 62, 93
  accumulation, B_6 deficiency .102, 103
    sucrose and KCl 104
  effect of ionization on proper-
    ties 62
  released from serum proteins . 11
  transport 97
β-Alanine 93
  in protein. 93
Amino acid, accumulation 114
  in biotin- and pantothenate-
    deficient cells 109
  effect of cell wall synthesis
    on 106
  stimulated by pyridoxal 97
  -activating enzymes 42
  analysis of peptides 7 and 8 . . . 14
  isomers, uncharged, molar re-
    fraction. 61, 62
  pools, osmotically active. 96
  residues, refraction. 57, 58, 59
  refractive index and spatial
    arrangement of 65
  transport, in bacteria. 96
    mechanism 111
    vitamin B_6 in 109
  uptake, in *E. coli* 112
  effect of vitamin deficiencies
    on 101
Amino acids, in animal protein . . 94
  in bacterial growth 118
  in cockroach protein 93

Amino acids (continued)
  differential responses to 118
  incorporation 41
  in lipide extracts 114
  molar refractions .57, 58, 59, 61, 62
  refractive indices . . . 54, 57, 58, 59
  vitamin carrier for 97
Aminoacyl, transfer 43
  sRNA ribosomes 42
Aminoadipic acid 100
Aminobutyric acid 100
$\propto$-Aminobutyric acid 58
$\propto$-Aminocaproic acid 58
Aminovaleric acid 100
$\propto$-Aminovaleric acid 58
Anlage hypothesis. . . . . . xiii, 2, 3, 4
Arginine 58, 93
Ascorbic acid, deficiency 68
  -deficient, animals 71
  granuloma, hydroxylation of
    proline by 74
  deprivation. 71
Asparagine 58, 100
Aspartic acid. 58, 93, 100
  released from serum proteins . 10
Aspartic transcarbamylase 132
Aspartic-glutamic transaminase . 102
ATP creatine phosphate kinase . . 5

B

Bacteria, cell walls 120
  composition 124
  depletion point 120
  lipide 123
  log cells 124
  membrane 122
  threonine-depletion cells. . .121, 124
  valine-depletion cells 121, 124
Bacterial growth, amino acids in 118
Bence-Jones, globulin. 6
  proteins 13, 15
Biosynthesis, of phosphates 128
  of plasma proteins, liver in . . . 17
  of serum proteins 4
Biotin deficiency, effect on
    amino acid uptake. 111

INDEX

Bovine serum albumin 60, 63
Brain acyl phosphatase, amino
    acid composition 130

C

C^{14}-amino acids 52
Carbamate kinase 132
Carbamyl phosphate, biosynthesis
    and utilization of 128
    enzyme, identity 128
    synthetase, activation by acetyl
        glutamate 133
      cold lability induced by acetyl
        glutamate 138
      effect on SH content and phys-
        ical properties 139
      mechanism of action 144
      synthesis and utilization of
        acetyl-P and formyl-P ... 142
N-Carbobenzoxy-4-ketoproline.. 75
Carboxypeptidase............ 5
α-Casein 60
Cell, membrane............. 105
    space 104
    wall biosynthesis.......... 114
    wall synthesis, effect on amino
        acid accumulation....... 106
Cellular differentiation 127
Ceruloplasmin............... 17
    biosynthesis 36
    synthesis 28
Chemical relationships among
    electrophoretic components
    of sera 5
Chicken serum 3
Chloramphenicol inhibition of li-
    poamino acid synthesis ... 115
Chymotrypsinogen B.......... 5
Collagen, formation 78
    synthesis 67
Common peptides........... 4, 9
Conalbumin................ 5
Cu^{64} acetate 18
Cystathionine 82
Cystathioninuria 83
Cystine.................. 58, 93
    biosynthesis 82
Cystinuria 82
Cytochrome C 5

D

Diglycine 61

E

Egg proteins 5
Electrophoretic separation,
    plasma mucoproteins. 21, 23, 24, 27
Enzymes, carbamyl-phosphate
    and acetyl-phosphate..... 128
L-Ethionine 37
Extracellular osmotic activity,
    accumulation capacity.... 106

F

Fermentation, energy require-
    ment 97
Fibrinogen 17
    biosynthesis 30, 31, 33, 36
Formyl phosphate, biosynthesis
    and utilization of 128

G

Gelatin.................. 60, 63
α-Globulin 20, 26, 34, 35
β-Globulin............ 20, 26, 35
γ-Globulin........ 12, 15, 26, 34, 35
    structure 15
Glutamate accumulation, α-amino
    and α-carboxyl groups ... 100
    effect of cell wall........ 108, 109
    effect of pH 100
    effect of sucrose and KCl on .. 103
    stimulation of 107
    structural specificity in 100
Glutamic acid 58, 93, 100
    conversion of L- to D- 97
    decarboxylase............ 102
    released from serum proteins . 10
    transport 97
Glutamine................ 58
Glutaric acid.............. 100
Glutathione 51
Glycine............. 58, 61, 62, 93
    released from serum proteins . 11
Glycolamide 62
Glycylaspartate 61

Glycylleucine 61
Glycyltyrosine.............. 61
Guanosine triphosphate 41

H

Heat denaturation of β-lacto-
   globulin, effect on refrac-
   tive index 64, 65
Hemoglobin, α-chain 5
  β-chain 5
Histidine................. 58, 93
Histones A, B, C 5
Horse serum albumin 60, 63
Human serum albumin 60, 63
Hydrolysis, partial, of serum
   proteins 9
Hydroxyglutamic acid 100
5-Hydroxylysine 68
Hydroxyproline 58
  formation of 67
Hydroxyprolyl-RNA 79
Hydroxyprolyl-sRNA 78

I

Isoleucine................ 58, 93

K

4-Keto-L-proline............ 75
Kinase, acetate and carbamate .. 132

L

Lactamide 62
α-Lactalbumin 60, 63
Lactobacillus arabinosus...... 96
β-Lactoglobulin 60, 63
  effect of heat denaturation on
   refractive index 64, 65
LDH 5
Leucine 58, 93
Lipoamino acid complexes, related to transport process . 115
  in protein synthesis 115
Lipoamino acid synthesis, inhibition by chloramphenicol... 115
Liver, in biosynthesis of plasma
   proteins 17
  perfusion, rat 18

Lorenz-Lorentz equation for mo-
   lar refraction 56
Lysine 18, 20, 34, 58, 93
Lysozyme............... 5, 60, 63

M

Methionine 58, 93
  oxidation 85
  sulfoxide ...!........... 93
    adsorption to proteins 92
    bound 89, 94
    in cockroach 85
    in proteins............. 94
    reduction with HCl 85
    soluble (free) 89
    synthesis in cockroach 86
Methylglutamic acid 100
Microbiological assay......... 118
Microsomes 42
Mitomycin C 34, 37
Molar atomic refractions 55
Molar ratio of ala to thr 6
Molar refraction, of alanine, ef-
   fect of ionization on 62
  amino acids 57, 58, 59, 61, 62
  ovalbumin, effect of ionization
   on 62
  peptides................ 61
  uncharged amino acid iso-
   mers 61, 62
Mucopeptide 106
Mucoproteins, plasma, electro-
   phoretic separation...... 21
Myeloma globulin........... 6, 15
  proteins............... 13, 14
Myokinase 5

N

NH_4^+, effect on glutamate accumulation 107
Nucleotides released 102

O

Ornithine transcarbamylase.... 131
Osmotically active pool....... 114
Ovalbumin 5, 60, 62, 63
  effect of ionization on proper-
   ties 62
Ovomucoid 5

INDEX

P

Pancreatic protein 5
Pantothenate-deficient cells, accumulation of amino acids . 111
Partial hydrolysis of serum proteins 9
Pepsin 60, 63
Peptide mapping, technique for . . 12
Peptide maps, of partial acid hydrolyzates 12
of serum proteins 13
Peptides 7 and 8 13
amino acid analysis 14
Peptides, molar refraction 61
refractive indices 60
Perfused rat liver 20, 35
Permeability barrier in bacteria. 112
Phenylalanine 58, 93
Phosphatidylglycerol, O-amino acid ester 114
Plasma lipoprotein, biosynthesis. 35
Plasma mucoproteins 17
electrophoretic separation . . 21, 23
Plasma proteins, autoradiograph of 22
electrophoretic separation . . 24, 27
liver in biosynthesis of 17
Proline 58, 93
accumulation, B_6 deficiency .102, 103
sucrose and KCl 104
conversion to hydroxyproline . 67, 78
hydroxylation 67
by ascorbic acid-deficient granuloma 74
transport 97
Propyl-sRNA 78
Protamine 2, 3
Protein 53
calculation of refractive index from amino acid composition 56
Proteins, refractive indices .54, 57, 60
effect of wave length on 64
and spatial arrangement of amino acid residues 65
specific refractive increments . 63
specific volume 57, 60
synthesis 41
Puromycin 37
Pyridoxamine, effect on glutamate accumulation 107

R

Rat albumin 5
Rat liver, perfused 18, 35
Refraction of amino acid residues .... .57, 58, 59
Refractions, molar atomic 55
Refractive index, of alanine, effect of ionization on 62
of amino acids .... .57, 58, 59
of amino acids, proteins, and related substances 54
determination 55
of β-lactoglobulin, effect of heat denaturation on 64, 65
of ovalbumin, effect of ionization on 62
of peptides 60
of proteins .... .56, 57, 60
effect of wavelength on 64
and spacial arrangement of amino acid residues 65
Ribonuclease 5, 60, 63
Ribonucleic acid, soluble 41
Ribonucleoprotein particles 52

S

Sera, electrophoretic components 5
Serine 58, 93
liberated from serum proteins . 10
Seromucoid 17
fractions 20
Serum, albumin 34
proteins 8
alanine released from 11
aspartic acid released from . 10
glutamic acid released from . 10
glycine released from 11
nature and origin 1
partial hydrolysis 9
peptide maps 13
serine released from 10
threonine released from 12
α-1-serum protein 8
α-2-serum protein 8
β-serum protein 8
γ-serum protein 8
Serum seromucoids 34
Specific refraction increments of proteins 63

Specific volume, of alanine,
    effect of ionization on 62
  of ovalbumin, effect of ionization on 62
  of proteins 57, 60
Stereospecificity in transport. . . 100
Streptococcus faecalis 118
Sucrose and KCl, accumulations of alanine and proline 104
  effects on glutamate accumulation 103
Sulfhydryl compounds 51

T

Teichoic acid 106
Threonine 58, 93
  released from serum proteins . 12
Transcarbamylase, aspartic . . . 132
  ornithine 131
Transport process, lipoamino acid complexes 115
Triglycine 61
Tritiated water, formation of from tritiated proline by granuloma 73
Trypsinogen 5

Tryptophan 58, 93
  -synthetase 5
Tryosine 58, 93

U

Urea cycle 128
  interrelations of P-enzyme metabolism with 129

V

Valine 58, 93
Vitamin B_6, carrier for amino acids in cellular transport . 102
  deficiency, effect on accumulation capacity 102
  proline and alanine accumulation 102
  participation in amino acid transport 109
Vitamin carrier for amino acids . 97

W

Walker tumor 25
Wavelength, effect on refractive index of proteins 64

QD
1
A355
#44

APR 18 1967